THE CIRCLES EFFECT
AND
ITS MYSTERIES

GEORGE TERENCE MEADEN

The Circles Effect Research Unit (CERES),
Tornado and Storm Research Organisation.

Terence Meaden

ARTETECH PUBLISHING COMPANY.
Bradford-on-Avon, Wiltshire, England.

Published by Artetech Publishing Company, 54 Frome Road, Bradford-on-Avon,
BA15 1LD, England. Tel: 02216 2482: Fax: 02216 5601.
(Publishers of the monthly international magazine *Journal of Meteorology* since 1975)

First published June 1989; second edition April 1990.

Printed by Dowland Press, Christchurch Street West, Frome, Somerset.

The authorized Japanese edition of this book, translated by
Professor Y. H. Ohtsuki, is published by the Maruzen Company Ltd., Tokyo, 1990.

ISBN 0 9510590 3 3

To my wife Anne Jacqueline
whose encouragement and patience
have been so helpful
during the long years
of this investigation

Terence Meaden was born in Trowbridge, Wiltshire, and educated at Trowbridge Boys High School and St Peter's College, Oxford University, subsequently taking a doctorate with research in low-temperature solid-state physics (involving the electrical and magnetic properties of metals) at Oxford and the Atomic Energy Research Establishment, Harwell. Post-doctoral appointments at the Universities of Oxford and Grenoble were followed by the tenured post of Associate Professor of Physics at Dalhousie University, Halifax, Canada. More recently, after returning to England Dr Meaden founded the Tornado and Storm Research Organisation, with its international magazine *The Journal of Meteorology,* specializing in research on atmospheric vortices, tornadoes, whirlwinds, waterspouts, and ball lightning. He has published extensively in physics and meteorology, including in 1966 a book on *The Electrical Resistance of Metals.* Another major occupation is archaeology, with particular interests in the Neolithic and Bronze Age periods of the world.

CONTENTS

Photographic credits: Figure 19, Rex Hutchinson; Figure 21, Stephen Broome (ref. *Probe Report);* Figure 25 supplied by V.-J. Ballester-Olmos; Figure 31, James Pickering; Figure 33, Christopher Wood, *Daily Express;* Figure 39, Mrs Olive Bessant; Figure 42, Ian Mrzyglod. The remainder are by the author.

Chapter One

PUZZLES IN THE CORN

Find out the cause of this effect;
Or rather say, the cause of this defect,
For this effect defective comes by cause.

Hamlet, ii.

1.1 INTRODUCTION

Since the summer of 1980 the author has inquired into an intriguing
scientific problem which has lately attracted the curiosity of the world. This is
the 'circles effect', a previously-unrecognized phenomenon in which neat
geometrical patterns appear in farmers' fields as flattened circles and rings
with sizes ranging from the diameter of a cartwheel, to that of a circus arena.
The sudden popularity of these puzzling circles is certainly due to the sense of
mystery that always surrounds an unknown phenomenon, particularly an
aesthetically-pleasing one which arrives unseen and carves intricate patterns
appearing to bear the stamp of intelligent planning (Figure 1).

Each summer in May or June fresh evidence appears – circular-symmetric
shapes firmly imprinted in the fields by the angled straws of a once-virgin crop.
Regarded from a distance, the uniform shapes recall the skill of the graphic
artist. The patterns attract the eye and stir the imagination. They invite endless
speculation from onlookers as to their origin, at times wild and humorous, at
others considered and grave. And every year, the precious evidence, so
exquisitely disposed but ageing and vulnerable, is pitilessly extinguished by
the remorseless advance of the combine harvester, that devouring monster
which like death 'ends and consumeth all' (Figure 2).

The search for a solution has followed those winding trails forever dividing
and lengthening which are familiar to scientists. What began as an ingenuous
desire to ascertain when and how plain single circles could be formed (the only
ones known at the beginning) has, in the wake of a multitude of unforeseeable
discoveries, evolved into an arduous, complex study – one which will have far-
reaching consequences in disciplines well removed from the one in which the
investigation began.

Fig.2: Fields at Bratton showing two doublets (one superimposed on an earlier one), a triplet, and a quintuplet, as photographed on 22 August 1987. The combine harvester has destroyed the quintuplet but the pattern remains easily discernible from the air.

Even by the end of 1983 the author had sufficient data to commence a book, but the volume begun at that time was soon split and split again. Indeed, so numerous had been the discoveries that each year's research has extended the work-load and further delayed attempts at completing the main book. Therefore in view of a continual demand from inquirers for a long-overdue survey of the circles effect, and because it has become increasingly onerous for me to withhold the secrets that I have harboured for so long, I offer the present work in the interim, with the aims of furnishing the background for a part of the research work (but only a part) and of responding to the main questions with which I have been besieged. Unfortunately, space restrictions limit the present book in two ways – by rationing the amount of detail *and* the range of topics to be treated. This means including no more than a pilot selection of representative case-histories, a factor always to be borne in mind as the reader progresses through the book.

From the beginning, reports were published in the *Journal of Meteorology* in order to alert the international scientific community to the importance of the observational side of the discoveries. By the end of 1989 two dozen articles had appeared, and for 1990 and 1991 it is expected that nearly every issue of the magazine will include articles on the circles effect, but until June 1989 I deliberately limited public theorizing to considering concepts on the vortex nature of the agent that creates the circles[1]. For this much was obvious to a professional physicist and experienced 'vortex-watcher' from the start, that the circles were laid out by a spinning effect originating naturally from sources within our atmosphere.

Since 1974 I had directed the Tornado and Storm Research Organisation, a consultative body concerned with the collection and analysis of data on tornadoes, whirlwinds, waterspouts, ball lightning, hailstorms and thunderstorms, so I was well acquainted with the recognized species of the whirlwind family and the fact that tornadoes are known to be accompanied by electromagnetic and discharge effects while the humble whirlwind is but *an electrostatic vortex* in disguise. However, for the new vortex, proof of associated electromagnetism was initially absent, until in 1983 the first clue was spotted. Although doubtful at first, I could see in aerial photographs of the quintuplet at Bratton what I suspected might be an 'ion race' (Sections 5.5 and 7.4), and from 1985 the accumulation of circumstantial evidence, followed by more direct evidence, gathered pace. In view of the necessity to marshal and assess a soaring mass of complex data (cf Section 7.3), the need for secrecy was paramount. Accordingly, no remarks on the *physical properties* of the vortex have, until now, been made in public; instead I have merely commented on possible atmospheric-mechanical origins for the vortex itself. This book, accordingly, is an introduction to mysteries on several levels – the circles, the vortices, their origins, and their dynamic and electromagnetic properties among others. And a start is made at supplying the answers.

1.2 THE CIRCLES

The circular-symmetric damage patterns range from simple individual circles, occasionally singly or doubly ringed, to more complex doublets, triplets, quadruplets, and quintuplets. Occasionally, triplets and quintuplets are found in combination with ringed varieties as well. Outlines of the principal patterns known to date are illustrated in Figure 3. Such has been the steady stream of discoveries in each new season that we do not doubt that other shapes remain to be found. (See pages 108-111 for the discoveries of 1989).

What can these patterns mean? Or as the mystics would say, "What messages are we being sent? Solving the patterns and their origins, deciding why a particular type should appear on one occasion and not on another, are the most fundamental questions to which we can address ourselves. Ultimately, it is going to be the theoretical atmospheric physicist who will successfully minister the full and correct answers.

Let us regard Figure 2 as an example. This is appealing for its accommodation within a single photograph of a compact array of fourteen circles, the product of four independent episodes happening inside four weeks. In a small area of land, not exceeding three acres in size, we find a quintuplet, a triplet, and a doublet superimposed on an earlier doublet. A complete

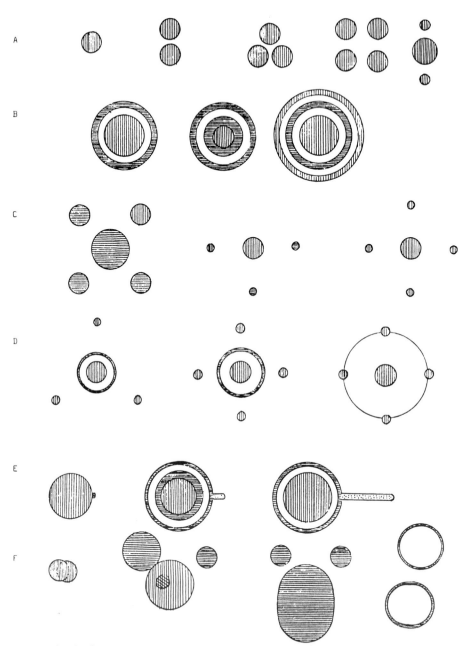

Fig.3: The chief varieties of circle-patterns discovered to date (not drawn to scale). Note that clockwise and anticlockwise variants have not been allowed for in this simplified résumé. Row A: Plain singles, doubles, triples, and quadruplets. Row B: Ringed singles. Row C: Quintuplets, including a 'defective' one with a satellite 'missing'. Row D: Multiplets with rings. Row E: Circles and ringed circles with radially-directed spurs. Row F: Superimposed singles and doubles; an ellipse with two singles; circular and elliptical rings.

explanation of the origin of this galaxy of designs constitutes a difficult but fascinating and rewarding problem in atmospheric dynamics, and its genuine importance for physics and meteorology will become clearer as we proceed through each chapter.

Our other works on the circles effect will go into numerous individual case-histories in detail, and will treat a number of other discoveries relevant to the problem which are not being mentioned at this time. Here, in order to limit the survey to about a hundred closely-written pages, we are obliged to restrict its scope by directing attention chiefly at the single crop-circle (ringed and unringed) and the perceived and predicted physical properties of its parent atmospheric-vortex. Nonetheless, we shall find it indispensable at times to bring facets of the impressive quintuplet circles into the discussion as well.

1.3 THE CIRCLE BEDS

The most typical feature, obvious even from a distance, is the sharp circular perimeter which separates the affected area from the undamaged corn (Figures 1, 2, 4, 5). Circular-axial symmetry is typical of nature's many fluid vortices, whether they develop in gaseous, liquid or plasma media. Another characteristic of the circles effect is a swirled or spiral flow, either clockwise or anticlockwise, whose incomparable traces are immediately spotted by the inquisitive visitor whether he approaches on foot or contemplates a circle with binoculars from an elevated standpoint (Figure 4).

Fig.4: A typical sharp-edged 8-metre circle with swirled spiral pattern rotating clockwise. Winterbourne Stoke, August 1987.

It is common for the stalks of corn to lie close to the ground, swirling outwards from a centre (Figure 5). Occasionally, a radial or curving-radial symmetry is noted instead. More rarely, a purely circular as distinct from a spiral array is seen. Sometimes the pattern made by the lying stalks is L-shaped from the centre, with the sharper curve near the perimeter, or is S-shaped from the centre in a manner denoting a directional change from initial anticlockwise to clockwise.

A theory must explain all these features, and account for those occasions when the crop is found to be *not* flattened to the ground by a powerful force but only partly bent over, as if the damaging agent had descended gently and managed to maintain a hovering position above the canopy of the crop!

The spiralling effect is the commonest pattern found in the flattened beds. In every instance, evidence of outward flow is present, sometimes turning to the left, sometimes to the right. In 1987 some 75 circles were archived for England, of which 66 were visited; 30 displayed clockwise rotation and 36 anticlockwise rotation. For 1988 numbers reached 110, of which 56 turned clockwise and 35 anticlockwise. Whereas indications for outward flow are always to be found, in one well-studied case (Headbourne Worthy, Hampshire, 1986) an initial outflow was superseded by subsequent inflow, as patently testified by the geometry of differential layering (Section 1.5). In fact many circle beds are complex multi-layered affairs; double-centering is fairly common (Figure 6). In short, even if a careful observer has time for only a fleeting inspection, he finds the inference unmistakeable, that whatever caused the damage must have come from above, and that, if it did not weaken and vanish *in situ,* it must have returned whence it came.

Fig.5: A tightly-turning anticlockwise spiral-circle. Beckhampton Down, September 1987.

1.4 THE CIRCLES ARE NO HOAX

We may be sure that none of the 500 circles personally examined by the author as background material for the present survey has been man-made. We are aware that some constructions have been attempted for fun, hoax, experiment, or entertainment (national newspaper rivalry 1983, television 1988, 1989), but such artifacts are easily distinguished from real circles. This is owed to the extremely intricate detail possessed by natural circles, for they are the end result of a quite complex sequence of happenings in the atmosphere. Because the beds are often multi-layered and double-centred, and the spirals occasionally change direction and terminate with curious edge effects, it means that the circles, and especially their beds, can never be duplicated in a manner that would deceive the experienced field investigator.

Moreover, some from among my professional colleagues who have expressed surprise at the discovery of the circles effect and questioned why it has not previously attracted the attention of scientists, prefer to deny its existence and reject the entire affair as a skilful hoax. Attitudes of negation are ill-considered and counter-scientific; one recalls those blinkered academics of last century who refused to accept that meteorites could be extraterrestrial despite the wealth of *prima facie* proof assembled in favour. Today's doubters of the ball-lightning phenomenon who oppose its existence for like reasons are similarly placed: for lack of a perfect theory, they choose to discard the testimony of even high-credibility witnesses in order to claim that ball lightning cannot happen. But as with all specialist topics in science, those who are unqualified to judge should refrain from comment. No-one, but *no-one,* should adopt a posture on the circles problem without first examining, in the company of an expert guide, at least a few circles in the field.

These circles are no elaborate hoax. They occur across the length and breadth of Britain. They are known from at least twelve countries in most continents, from the U.S.A. and Canada to South America, and from Europe to the U.S.S.R., Japan, Australia, Tasmania and New Zealand. In Europe circles have been reported from France, Italy, Switzerland, Austria, and Scandinavia, besides England and Wales. And in Britain circles are known from 26 counties. Many types of crop are represented: wheat, barley, oats, rye, maize, rape, mustard, sugarbeet, runner beans, soy beans, tick beans, spinach, tobacco and rice. To these we may add grass, reeds, swamp-vegetation, sand, dirt, and snow, among others. Circles-related ground phenomena have also been reported from Spain, Germany and South Africa.

Correspondents have sent me more than twenty accounts of circles-effect events which date from before 1980, while literature discoveries and interviews with farmers have added to their number. A few of these circles are complex. Mark Stenhoff and a colleague saw a ringed circle with two plain ones in the Bishopstrow Parish of Wiltshire twenty years ago, while types of double-ringed circles have been reported from fields near Evenlode (Gloucestershire, 1960) and Twywell (Northamptonshire, 1977). The oldest accounts received from correspondents date back to 1918 (a large plain circle in a field of beans or oats in Kent) and 1936 (near Aberystwyth). Recently, the case of a ringed circle dated August 1678 has come to light (*J. Meteorology*, November 1989). Not only would generations of hoaxers have to be involved, but they would need fine skills to lay out patterns with the complex beds and edge effects which are part of the circles effect, besides, on many occasions, having to demonstrate their dexterities at night in bad-weather conditions. And they would need enviable staying power to fake the 250-plus circles we found in 1989, many of which were deep in the countryside and spotted only during aircraft surveys. So how many hundreds more existed that we did not find? One may certainly infer very many on the basis of statistical scaling[2]. Lastly, there is the testimony of recent *eye-witnesses,* for the author knows of three separate occasions, all in daylight, when circles were watched *as they were being made,* the corn or grass lying itself flat before their eyes.

We shall in fact show that every strand of evidence assembled so far points to atmospheric vortices as the fons et origo of the circles effect, as we have repeatedly said since 1980. This book is accordingly largely about atmospheric vortices – volumes of air spinning rapidly about an axis. What is more, and this is highly stimulating for scientists and the public alike, these vortices, in common with other natural atmospheric vortices, have the capacity to be ionized, at least partially, meaning that they are accompanied by electrical, optical and acoustic effects. *Therefore some are visible in the dark as balls of light.* This considerably expands the scope of the inquiry by taking it into electromagnetism and other disciplines and increases the scientific importance of the effect manyfold (Chapters 4 et seq).

On the other hand, we shall not neglect to point out that alternative ideas to the author's vortex theory have been advanced to account for the circles effect, although on no firm ground and sometimes jocularly. These are summarized in Section 7.2.

1.5 BASIC DEDUCTIONS ABOUT THE VORTEX MECHANISM USING GROUND-TRACE ANALYSIS

When the vortex strikes, a pattern of damage is frozen into the corn. Careful examination allows us to deduce basic facts about the physical properties of the vortex. Both the obvious centre and the outwardly-directed array of stalks are witness to a once-strong movement away from the middle. The severity of the flattening testifies to the strength of the force. The majority of circles being spiral-centred, the lying straws of the crop follow either a clockwise spiral or an anticlockwise spiral (Figure 5). As mentioned already, the straw flow-lines sometimes have S-shaped profiles indicating a mixed twisting effect.

The spiral or radial 'centre' does not always lie at the geometrical midpoint of the circle, nor is the circle necessarily a mathematically-perfect circle. It is merely by convenience that we call the various forms 'circular', whether they are exactly so or not. There are two principal reasons for imperfect circularity.

Fig.6: The main circle of a quintuplet on Beckhampton Down, July 1988. The ranging rod and camera equipment have been placed at the two centres of this clockwise spiral-circle.

Firstly, while the circles are being formed, minor lateral movements of the entire spinning air-mass cause the spiral-centre to drift. Movements of less than half-a-metre are common, above a metre (as in the circle photographed in Figure 6) more exceptional. The result is that some circles become double-centred or even multi-centred while their circumferences suffer deformation, usually slight. Secondly, some, and probably many, circles are created by initially-downward forces which are applied at angles other than 90 degrees to the final ground trace.

A prominent exception to the usual indication for spiral outward flow was found in a Hampshire barley-field in August 1986. The survey proved that a vortex had initially scribed a circle with an outwardly-directed anticlockwise veining (as revealed by the directional ordering of an inferior layer of the straws), but that a second stage had evolved in which the superior straws had shifted again to finish as an anticlockwise-inward pattern (Figure 7). This suggested that the parent vortex, having struck the crop and expanded the area of damage to a diameter of some 17 metres, afterwards contracted its contact-area as it 'took off' again.

The evidence of the majority of circles points to the arrival by descent of a spinning vortex and to its probable weakening or dissipation *in situ*. Lifetimes, as judged by the time to scribe the spiral-circle, are short – a few seconds as a rule. This is known from the observations of eye-witnesses (Section 2.2), and can also be deduced from the nature of the damage, such as a lack of significant drifting that might arise during an extended event lasting a minute or more

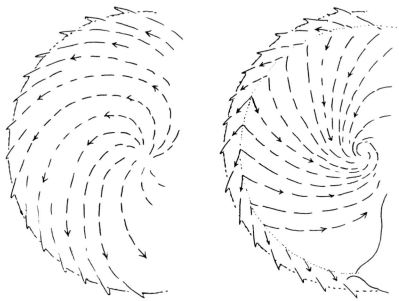

Fig.7: Diagrammatic representations of the straw flow-lines forming lower and upper layers of an anticlockwise circle at Headbourne Worthy, Hampshire, August 1986 (the right-hand drawing is after C. Andrews, *J. Meteorology*, ref. 3).

and which might be expected to transform circular damage into a lengthy trail (very few cases of damage trails are known, as distinct from quasi-circular damage events).

Besides the eye-witness accounts to the circles-effect (to be given in Section 2.2), we can cite eye-witness reports for *related sightings* which involved spinning vortices scouring hollows into cropless soil (Section 1.7). We also have a number of well-authenticated incidents of witnesses being struck by abnormally-powerful, 'humming' localized spinning winds at times of day or night when normal whirlwind or tornado development was meteorologically impossible (examples Sections 2. 3, 6.6 *infra*). Other accounts from the CERES archive include gyrating winds which struck buildings *by descent* during the evening, early morning or night, *some coming from a clear sky!* Considering everything together regarding such eye-witness evidence, we conclude that the lifetime of most circle-scribing events at ground level does not usually exceed some ten seconds in general, and may be much shorter; however, inferred hovering times are another matter and may be very much longer.

1.6 CIRCLES WITH RADIAL SYMMETRY

Thus far, we have mentioned clockwise and anticlockwise spiral-centred circles. These are marked out by a species of vortex that descends from above and spins either to the left or to the right. Surveys of nearly five hundred circles in 1987, 1988 and 1989 suggest that the two senses are about equally represented on a global scale, although certain locations only seem able to produce circles of a particular spin-direction. For instance, every circle known for Cheesefoot Bottom, near Winchester, Hampshire, has as yet been clockwise in its sense of direction (the anticlockwise rings surrounding some of the clockwise circles is a different matter). On the other hand, some crop-circles are characterized by what we term a 'star-burst' appearance and display little or no evidence of rotational effects over a large part of their diameter. The circle formations at Chilcomb (Hampshire) in 1987 (Figure 8) and Oadby (Leicestershire) in June 1988 were typical.

The stalks flattened radially in this way are usually pressed so hard to the ground that no investigator can deny that there has been a seriously violent impact with the crop. Sometimes the radial effect extends as far as the perimeter, which is then not sharp; at other times, as the perimeter is neared, a spiral turn commences (always to the right) and the flowlines assume a hockey-stick or L-appearance. Occasionally, only the central metre or so of a medium-to-large circle exhibits a radial blast, beyond which the typical slow spiral sets in. We conclude that in all radial-blast or star-burst cases the downward vertical velocity of the vortex was initially very much greater than its horizontal tangential velocity at the periphery of the vortex.

Fig.8: The effect of a powerful radial burst is to press the crop very hard against the ground This was at Chilcomb, near Winchester, August 1987. Further from the centre a clockwise development commences, until at the circumference the flowlines are almost parallel to the unbroken wall of standing wheat.

A clear-cut incident displaying pure star-burst damage happened in Tamagata Prefecture, Japan, late one evening on 9 August 1986, and was studied by Yamaguchi and Namiki[4]. The three-metre rayed circle was defined by the lie of flattened reeds in the mud of a garden pond from which the water had been blasted away. This incident is highly relevant to our inquiry because of subsidiary acoustic and optical effects noted by the occupants of the nearby house, and we shall return to consider this incident in a later chapter (Section 4.4).

1.7 CIRCULAR HOLLOWS

Sometimes the pressure is so acute that a hollow or crater is scoured into the land-surface, or water ejected from the area of a swamp or a pond. Crater effects, like star-burst ones, signify a rapid descent of an energetic force at a speed which so much exceeds the spin-rate as to mask the identity of the latter.

An unidentified crater which could be a splendid example of this type of episode appeared in a potato field at Charlton (Wiltshire), not far from Shaftesbury (Dorsetshire) in July 1963 (see Section 4.6 below). Although no eye-witnesses were at hand to see this happen, it is logical to suppose that the earth was readily displaced in the blast because of its softness following a long wet spell.

When a vortex impacts hard earth, it is scarcely possible to blast out a crater but the result can be as interesting if witnesses are present as this next account shows. The source is *Scientific American* (1880)[5] where it is recorded that two citizens of East Kent, Ontario, were in a field belonging to one of them "when they heard a sudden loud report, like that of a cannon. They turned just in time to see a cloud of stones flying upward from a spot in the field. Surprised beyond measure they examined the spot, which was circular and about 16 feet across, but there was no sign of an eruption nor anything to indicate the fall of a heavy body there. The ground was simply swept clean. They are quite certain that it was not caused by a meteorite, an eruption of the earth, or a whirlwind".

We agree; it was not caused by a summer fair-weather whirlwind (which is what the anonymous writer meant). It is more likely the work of an unseen vortex of the circles-effect type and whose agility at 'sweeping' the ground clean arrived from above and gave rise to the cloud of dust and stones in the counterflowing air current. As we shall see (Section 2.2), this account is not dissimilar from the 1983 eyewitness sighting of Melvyn Bell who was fortunate to watch a true spiral-circle being created one evening in a wheatfield.

1.8 RINGED CIRCLES

In 1986 crop-circles with an encircling ring were found. Further cases have turned up since, and more recently circles with double rings. The complete range known to date is included in Figure 3.

Fig.9: The double rings of a multi-ringed circle in a field of barley near Longwood, Hampshire, June 1988. The flow is clockwise in the main circle and outer ring but is counter-clockwise in the intermediate ring.

The ring of a singly-ringed circle has often been found with the corn flattened in the opposite sense to that of the main circle. With double rings the flow in the outermost ring is contrary to the flow in the inner one. A photograph of a Hampshire double-ringed circle dating from June 1988 is provided in Figure 9. In August 1989 a triple-ringed circle appeared in Wiltshire.

Walking along one of these rings is like keeping to a narrow walled lane. There are no indications of cycloidal or running-spiraliform effects. The stalks lie flat and almost parallel, just turning slightly to conform with the curvature of the perimeter (Figure 10). The width is typically one to two metres. Circumferential lengths of a hundred metres have been measured a number of times; the longest perimeter known is 125 metres. Whatever the nature of the air-pressure that presses the stalks over in this manner it certainly exercises an amazingly fine degree of control.

What kind of wind can confine itself with such precision? Obtaining a solution to this takes us a long way towards gaining a total understanding of the grand problems at issue. The situation is reminisent of the waterspout which similarly has up to two very thin sheaths around its column, yet no explanation, I believe, has ever been given for the physical origin of these familiar sheaths. For the circles-effect vortex, we have alluded to the answer already (Section 1.1); it is an induced 'ion race', the crop being flattened by a wind of ionized air. Our explanation for this needs considerable introduction, however, and is not reached until Chapter 5.

Fig.10: View taken from the floor of the inner ring shown in Figure 9.

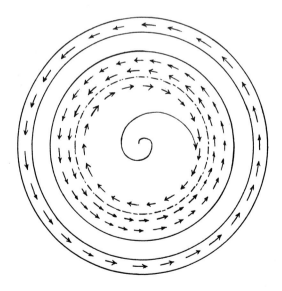

Fig.11: Plan to demonstrate the contra-flow situation discovered inside the main circle of single-ringed circles noted in Oxfordshire, Hampshire and Wiltshire in July 1986.

A further puzzle is the finding that circles can have dual counter-rotating sections within a single circular bed. Where this has happened, it has been within the main circle of a singly-ringed circle system (Figure 11). Three instances are known at the time of writing, all from the same summer – 1986. They came one each from Hampshire, Wiltshire, and Oxfordshire, and were formed in the same month of July within three weeks of one another at most. At the internal boundary inside the main circle the straws lie touching one another but in opposite directions! On looking at it, one is mindful of the skill and art of the conjurer. What kind of airflow can achieve this miracle of refined aerial engineering?

1.9 CIRCLES WITH OUTWARDLY-DIRECTED SPURS

Lastly, we introduce one of the most mystifying of all the circles-effect puzzles to be solved in the single-circle mysteries; this it owes to its unexpected break with circular-axial symmetry. It is the finding of a finite spur which starts at the perimeter of the ring surrounding a single plain circle and is directed outward along a radius. With singly-ringed systems the radial spur can acquire an important length. A three-metre spur was found at Childrey (Oxfordshire) in 1986, and a fourteen-metre spur in South Wiltshire in 1987 (Figure 12). Full details will be given elsewhere, but a brief discussion is held in Section 5.10 *infra*. Short radial spurs are occasionally seen emanating from the edge of simple (unringed) circles. The example in Figure 13 demonstrates the sharpness of edge between straws lying tangential to the circumference within the circle and radially within the spur.

Fig.12: A ringed circle with a 14-metre long outwardly-directed radial spur which has followed the area of weakness stimulated by the presence of tractor lanes.

Fig.13: The edge of a spur showing the mutually perpendicular flowlines between a radial spur and the perimeter of a non-ringed circle.

Having briefly reviewed the major puzzles offered by the ground traces of the circles effect, we must next allow the several eye-witnesses to speak for themselves.

Chapter Two

THE TESTIMONY OF WITNESSES

In the mouth of two or three witnesses
shall every truth be established.

II Corinthians

2.1 THE VALUE OF EYE-WITNESS EVIDENCE

In this chapter we allow eye-witnesses to speak for themselves. It is their testimony, unsolicited and possessed of a high degree of credibility, that stands alongside the ground-trace studies at the nucleus of the new discipline under investigation. Let us follow the advice of Dr Lardner: "When any new and unexplained phenomenon offers itself to our enquiry, the first duty of the investigator is to inform himself, with the most scrupulous accuracy, of all the circumstances, however minute, which accompany it; and if past observation cannot answer all circumstantial enquiries which his understanding may suggest as necessary, he must patiently wait the recurrence of a like phenomenon, and diligently observe. When he shall thus have collected all the circumstances that can be imagined to throw light on its origin, he will then be in a condition to justify an enquiry into its cause"[6].

We begin with spiral-circles. We know of three occasions when eye-witnesses have watched spiral-circles being created naturally in cereal crops or grass. One of these is exactly dated. For another the date is known to within a week. It is by the receipt of eye-witness accounts that we shall most rapidly advance our understanding of the forces that govern circle-making, just as it will be by instrumented observations that we shall eventually come to understand the physical processes which create the vortices. We therefore appeal for additional witnesses to come forward as we have reason to believe that there are others who have been fortunate enough to attend such spectacles. Their information is crucial because it permits us to establish how and in what sequence the various parts of the circle systems are laid down, besides allowing us to reconstruct the circumstances of the weather and to some extent the state of the atmosphere. When we can predict in general terms the meteorological conditions under which the circles form, we shall be able to direct experimental resources to the best advantage.

Brief accounts, with commentaries, of the three known observations follow in Section 2.2. Afterwards we cite the evidence of people who have watched non-circle-making vortices behaving so strangely as to suggest that had a crop been present then a circle may have formed (Sections 2.3 – 2.5). The chapter concludes with additional case histories involving vortices which appear to be closely related physically to the general problem under investigation (Sections 2.6 – 2.8).

2.2 THREE EYE-WITNESS ACCOUNTS OF CIRCLES-EFFECT INCIDENTS

One fine evening at the beginning of August 1983 Mr Melvyn Bell was horse-riding on the slopes of Great Cheverill Hill on the northern side of Salisbury Plain, not far from New Zealand Farm (Figure 14). Becoming aware of dust which suddenly started spiralling up from a wheatfield 50 to 60 metres away to the north of the lane, he watched from his high viewpoint while a circle, diameter estimated at 10-12 metres, was laid out in the corn. He considered that the time taken to make the circle was no more than a couple of seconds. For some moments dust and debris spun upwards and fell back again, chiefly around the edge of the circle[7].

This plain statement regarding the visible levitation of dust and debris attests to the action of the counterflowing currents around the perimeter. We

Fig.14: Melvyn Bell who witnessed the formation of a spiral-circle in a field of wheat on the slopes of Great Cheverill Hill, Wiltshire, at the beginning of August 1983 as the sun was setting.

Fig.15: Straws lying horizontally on the canopy of the crop adjacent to a freshly-formed circle. This is the result of counterflowing aerial currents spinning straw debris out of the bed of the circle and tossing it beyond the circumference.

have seen evidence of this in analogous ways on several occasions. In August 1987, for instance, during a good dry spell when the ground became hard and dusty our patience at making regular site inspections was rewarded by chancing upon several freshly-formed circles about which broken straws and leaves lay on the undamaged crop just beyond the circumference. The debris had clearly got there in the way that Melvyn Bell described (Figure 15).

Some years earlier the formation of a circle was watched by a large number of people as it appeared in long grass one summer's evening near Starr Hill, also known as Middle Hill, in West Wiltshire. "Suddenly the grass began to sway before our eyes and laid itself flat in a clockwise spiral, just like the opening of a lady's fan. A perfect circle was completed in less than half a minute, all the time accompanied by a high-pitched humming sound. It was still there the next day".[8]

This account is intriguing for the manner in which the circle developed – 'like the opening of a lady's fan'. Confirmation that circles can be formed in this fashion has come quite recently from another source. In a letter to the author an eye-witness, Mr Barnes, of Wiltshire, recounted an event which reference to weather diaries allowed me to pinpoint as Saturday 3 July 1982.

"I have been meaning to write to you for some time on the subject of corn circles. About six or seven years ago I was fortunate to see one of these form in a field at Westbury. It happened on a Saturday in early July just before six in the evening after a thunderstorm earlier that afternoon; in fact it was still raining slightly.

My attention was first drawn to a 'wave' coming through the heads of the cereal crop in a straight line at steady speed; I have since worked this out to be about fifty miles an hour. The agency, though invisible, behaved like a solid object throughout and did not show any fluid tendencies, i.e. no variation in speed, line or strength. There was no visual aberration either in front, above or below the advancing line. After crossing the field in a shallow arc the 'line' dropped to a position about 1 o'clock and radially described a circle 50-75 feet radius in about four seconds. The agency then disappeared".

A useful sketch was included, and a site visit and interviews followed. A full discussion is held elsewhere[9], but some discussion is held in Section 3.5. A simplified drawing based on a sketch supplied by the witness is given in Figure 16.

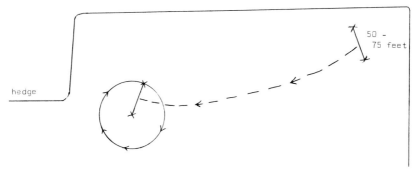

Fig.16: Simplified sketch map after the original drawn by Mr Barnes who witnessed the formation of a big-diameter circle at Westbury, Wiltshire, on Saturday, 3 July 1982. Time of day was 5.50 p.m. summer time (1650 G.M.T.) when the witness reported a 'line' traversing the field until it suddenly pivoted at one end and described a circle in about four seconds, all the time accompanied by a humming sound.

We have numerous eye-witness accounts on record of incidents which involved spinning systems of various kinds. Some of these are summarized in this chapter and a few others are used in later chapters. This token selection may be taken to demonstrate the range of information available in our files.

2.3 WITNESSES IN THE WIND

We commence with the tale of two ladies and their dog at Westbury, Wiltshire. In October 1986 the ladies were crossing a field behind their house which is a kilometre from the escarpment of Salisbury Plain to the east. Three months earlier two spiral-circles had manifested themselves in this field which was then planted with wheat. The biggest was about fifteen metres across. Although the crop was harvested in August the field had not afterwards been ploughed, so the remains of the circles could still be seen. Skies were grey that day and the afternoon wet but as the rain came to a halt the ladies went out with the dog. The time was 1615 GMT and the date 24 October, as confirmed by a diary entry.

"When we reached the spot where the circles had been, we were suddenly caught up in a terrific whirlwind. It came without warning, no gradual build-up. We could hardly stand up against it and *it was difficult to get one's breath*. It was all spinning, with the noise of the wind. Bing (the dog) went wild. Altogether quite frightening, but when we finally got past this spot the atmosphere was calm again and there was no wind at all. We concluded it must be whirlwinds which cause these circles".

The wind-of-the-day was westerly, as judged by weather charts. The day was sunless and cool[10], conditions which render conventional whirlwinds wholly improbable. Yet it was certainly a whirling vortex that hit the ladies, for its reported characteristics firmly suggest that it had most likely 'come from above', and indeed may well have been the type of spinning wind which we know as the 'circles-effect vortex'. The difficulty with breathing is to be noted. The likely importance of this clue, and the behaviour of the dog, will be clarified when we offer an explanation in a later chapter (Section 6.10).

2.4 DEVASTATION IN THE GARDEN

Next we turn to Cheddar, Somerset, July 1984, where an outdoor rotary clothes line suffered surprise damage. Notice that the *downward* bending of one of its struts implies a downward force and pressure from the wind.

"Mrs Nelly Taylor checked the washing on her rotary clothes line and went indoors. A few seconds later she went out again and found washing strewn all over the garden. The remaining washing was wound round the pole, which was slightly askew. One of the quarter-inch-thick (6mm thick) struts had been strongly bent downwards. Strawberry plants stacked in neat heaps were also strewn everywhere. This happened in less than a minute and without a sound. The weather was mild with hardly any wind". *(Sunday Express)*.

We have several descriptions of gardens and sheds suffering inexplicable damage at night-time, even on what appeared to be *quiet* nights with little or no wind (like the Cumnor Hill, Oxford, house-owner whose toolshed roof was found one morning in autumn 1984 shifted from its correct position and left oddly at an angle). This next case from Norton Bavant, Wiltshire involved a household garage which was a couple of hundred metres from the sites of two well-investigated spiral-circles in the adjoining field of wheat. One of these circles can be seen in Figure 17. The resident Mr Sharp explained how *not long after dawn*, it being already daylight, on an otherwise calm, clear windless morning he heard the noise of what he called a 'whirlwind' suddenly

Fig.17: A newly-formed circle in a field not far from the garage building which was struck by a descending vortex after dawn on a fine morning in July 1988. Michael Rutty is standing at one centre of this double-centred vortex-circle.

battering the *roof* of the garage next to his house. It did not approach in the progressive way that is usual for the mobile summer whirlwinds with which he is familiar, and which are heard coming as they approach from a distance. Instead it arrived suddenly as though *dropping* from above, but the noise soon stopped and the strong brick-built garage was found to be unharmed[11].

In the same way that fields, gardens, garages and people get struck without warning by wind-pressure violence, so do houses and motor-cars. So we now look at incidents involving houses, while leaving the still more important automobile cases for Chapter 6.

2.5 HOUSES GET A BATTERING

During the course of compiling T.O.R.R.O.'s extensive data-bank of British tornadoes, waterspouts, whirlwinds, ball lightning, etc, Michael Rowe and the author have had to consider the bona fides of the two thousand plus tornado/whirlwind/vortex events which have come to our attention. One in particular was outstanding for the difficulty in placing it correctly – an evening occurrence at Deighton, nine kilometres south of York, on 23 June 1963. The day had been warm and dry, and none of the *Daily Weather Report* stations reporting to the Meteorological Office had had showers or rain. A tornado was impossible, and at a time so late in the evening a land-devil whirlwind seemed wholly improbable too. From the *Yorkshire Gazette* we quote:

"Mrs Gwen Lofthouse was sitting in the front room of her home . . . when the whirlwind struck. 'There was a rushing sound and a rumble, just like an aeroplane or thunder. Then in a split second, everything seemed to blow. I looked through the windows and sand from the bottom of the garden was going round and round in the sky. Then I saw something falling past the windows . . . tiles were streaming down from the roof in a big shower. Then suddenly everything was still. It was uncanny'"[12]

Or consider this happening at breakfast time in fine quiet weather in the village of Crockerton, Wiltshire: Ted and Gwen Davies on hearing a terrific din thought the noise emanated from the flapping of birds' wings rustling over their thatched rooftop and crackling round the chimney. Mrs Davies said: 'Our rafters shook and the windows rattled. We thought all the birds in these parts were migrating'. Mr Davies spoke of 'the loud clattering from the chimney and a gale-force wind'. They hastened outside but there were no birds. 'There was not a trace of wind. The sky was blue, the air cold yet invigorating'. The date was 25 March 1965[13]. A dozen similar cases could be cited, some of them nocturnal events.

2.6 SOME OBSERVATIONS OF VAPOUR-FILLED LOW-LEVEL VORTICES

Next it is the turn of vortices which are rendered visible by direct condensation effects.

Tornadoes are invariably accompanied by that well-known highly-typical sight the vapour-filled tapering funnel, pendant from a convective cloud. The spin is so intense that water vapour condenses in the fast rotating core, which thereby designates the envelope of fastest winds. Land-devils or dust-devils being *fair-weather* whirlwinds do not become visible in this manner. The air is too dry for condensation effects, and the spin-rate does not attain the magnitude of tornado speeds. This means that devils are invisible unless or until they levitate light debris such as dust, dirt, sand and straw, etc.

So what are we to make of the meek-looking vortices spotted near Avebury on Thursday 16th June 1988 by farm-hand Roy Lucas. The night had been clear but fog had developed and shifted upwards to conceal the sky with stratus. At 0715 GMT Mr Lucas was in a tractor cab cutting the grass verges of a by-way leading to the famous Neolithic causewayed enclosure Windmill Hill when he saw 80 metres distant a narrow spinning column of what he took to be opaque white 'smoke' or vapour surrounded by an outer transparent sheath (Figure 18). He said that it emerged out of thin air and the core disappeared suddenly the same way, but the residues of the outer section lasted longer and drifted for a few seconds in the light north-east wind. Overall diameter of the vortex was four or five metres. A repeat performance was noted a few seconds later in the same place and five minutes later a little further away. A detailed treatment of this marvellous episode has been

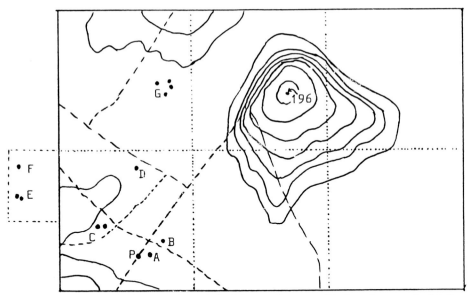

Fig.18: Map showing the locations (A and B) of the small vapour-filled vortices seen by Mr Roy Lucas (who was at P altitude 163m) and the sites of ten vortex-circles (C, D, E, F, G) relative to Windmill Hill. Altitudinal contours of 165 metres or more are indicated. The wind had frequently been from east to north-east during the preceding month, and was light north-east on the day of the sighting (16 June 1988).

published in the *Journal of Meteorology*[14]. The main point arising is that the geostrophic wind was light north-east and the low eminence of Windmill Hill was a kilometre distant in that direction. Vortex development in its lee in very humid air appears to be a reasonable explanation.

A not-unrelated situation seems likely for a Scottish vortex case, for which the photograph of Figure 19 refers[15]. The clear account provided by an observant fisherman emphasizes that the motion in the vortex was upwards.

'Could I explain our experience last year (7 May 1983) while trout fishing on Carron Reservoir between Denny and Fintry and surrounded on one side by the Carron Forest. We had three boats with three fishers per boat. About 11 a.m. there had been very little wind and the trees were covered by a Scots mist or hoar. I witnessed an upward movement to low cloud. At first I thought it was a woodcutters fire but never heard any of the usual saw and tractor sounds. Then the Scots mist or hoar seemed to move (inwards) along the tree tops to a central position (and) then being moved upwards to this low cloud. I now knew it was some sort of suction as there were no signs of strong winds. I took two photographs which I enclose'.

It was fortunate that the air was so humid that day. The Scots mist which covered the trees implies near 100% humidity, the condition which allows a simple vortex, otherwise transparent in drier air, to become visible. The vortex

Fig.19: A huge eddy vortex (not a tornado) which formed over a forest canopy adjacent to the Carron Reservoir on the border between Strathclyde and Central Region in Scotland. The photograph was taken by Mr Rex Hutchinson on 7 May 1983. The vortex, in the lee of the mountain in the near distance, remained stationary throughout the period of observation.

was not a funnel cloud which grew downwards in the manner of a tornado or waterspout. It developed *in situ* by a flow that was inwards and upwards, as proved by the movement of the mist, and its position did not change. Being in the lee of the hill which can be seen in the photograph, it was plainly an eddy vortex or eddy whirlwind generated by flow around the hill. Such vortices are relatively common when hills are in the vicinity of bodies of water because the humidity criterion renders them visible. Dozens of eddy-vortex cases for the Scottish and English lakes are stored in our data bank. In the next chapter (Section 3.2-3.4) we shall find that this may be regarded as an upward rotating vortex of the geophysical columnar type initiated by flow past a topographical obstacle. Its likely relevance to the circles-effect problem will then be clarified.

2.7 REPORT OF A SIMPLE CLOUD VORTEX WITH OPTICAL EFFECTS

We are now in a position to consider a rather similar account from southern England. At the same time another factor of crucial moment is introduced, viz. luminosity!

The place was the north-western side of Longleat Woods, not more than two kilometres south-east of Cley Hill, a steep-sided chalk knoll jutting 60 metres above the plain west of Warminster. On 17 August 1969 William Seal who was in West Street 'espied' at a distance estimated as 1½ to two kilometres 'a glowing reddish kidney-shaped object with an orange aura. His wife joined him . . . and the two stood watching in the warm air as the mysterious object hovered over Longleat Woods for five minutes. The glow then dulled considerably and the object began to disperse, thinning in density without actually changing shape. After another four minutes it had gone completely. Entranced, the couple continued to gaze at the clear night sky, attention glued to the same spot. Once again the puzzling object materialised, glowing fitfully this time, faded once more and vanished within a few minutes . . . Two months later on a brisk October evening, William observed a weird white fog hazing the same area. It was drifting lazily across the woodland, in the sky; then altered direction and wisped woollily in the opposite flight path, slowly rocking back and forth like a gigantic and pulsating blanket until it was eventually still, motionless. For a moment there was a flashing glare of light in that section of sky, then the eerie mist-form commenced fading to mere puffballs of cosmic energy. Inside five minutes it had left the scene entirely'.[16]

The wind direction on the first occasion was light north-westerly as judged using the *Daily Weather Report* of the Meteorological Office for Boscombe Down and Wiltshire generally. This implies that the phenomenon developed in the lee of Cley Hill for a north-west wind. It is a pity that for the second occasion the exact date is not known but the nature of the movement of the mist-form again suggests a lee-effect. The reddish-coloured luminosity for the first event and the flash of light for the second are of fundamental importance for the current investigation because they provide a link between optical effects and topographically-induced vorticity.

This same lofty eminence could be a topographical obstacle responsible for another event some years later, but this time to the south-west of the hill. The date was Sunday 14th May 1977, when the general weather conditions were quietly anticyclonic over southern Britain. Observing from Cley Hill Cottage, Whitbourne Springs, near Corsley Heath, Miss J. McCormick awoke at around 01 GMT. In a letter she wrote:

'May I say I do not know what woke me up. I went to the bedroom window and at first saw nothing but darkness. It was absolutely pitch-dark in the garden, although on looking left I could see clearly the outline of Cley Hill itself. To the right of the window is the start of the grounds of Longleat. I noticed, after what must have been ten seconds, a light which was shining from the right – I assumed on to the garage which was facing right. I turned to look in the direction from which I thought the light was coming, and noticed a 'heavy mist' patch hanging on its own about 35 feet from the bedroom window. I looked again to ensure I was not seeing things that really were not there; and this time I was reassured! The mist got brighter; not *really* bright, but bright in comparison with the darkness of the garden. It lowered and formed into a bell-shaped outline. The shape was very prominent, although the light was only *within* the shape itself, and around the edges it appeared to be very 'fuzzy'. It then intensified into a brilliant white for a split-second, and was gone! . . . My fiancé also saw this object about a hundred yards away, on a slope that is within Longleat grounds. In all, the time must have been no more than five minutes (accounting for the time elapsing between my sighting and that of my fiancé)'.[17]

This sighting has similarities with others in this chapter. By its very symmetry the bell-shape suggests a spinning motion about a vertical axis. As with the previous incident a mist-form exudes luminous radiation which terminates with increased optical emission. Many other incidents are on record, of which a few are given in later sections, but we chose to concentrate for the time-being on the environs of Cley Hill for reasons to be clarified in Section 3.3. Having introduced optical effects in connection with small-scale vortices let us now turn to acoustic phenomena.

2.8 ACOUSTIC EFFECTS ACCOMPANYING VORTICES

We find in general that most occasions when witnesses are in close proximity to atmospheric vortices acoustic effects are noted, and sometimes luminous and electromagnetic effects too. The eye-witness at Westbury who witnessed the corn circle forming before his gaze (Section 2.2) reported a simultaneous rustling and hissing. In an interview he told me: 'The rustling was the noise of the falling corn, while the hissing emanated from the agent itself'. At Starr Hill the formation of the grass circle was accompanied by a humming sound.

A correspondent Mr Dennis Howard wrote to me in August 1988 to tell me of a loud, unpleasant buzzing or humming sound that he and his wife heard at 01 GMT when staying at Bolnhurst, Bedfordshire, twenty years earlier. The next morning they found a recently-formed *precise circle* with a burning appearance in an adjacent field of beans. The undamaged beans, supported by canes, were standing between "at least waist and eye high". "Usually our host's dogs would race into those beans and one would see the beans moving and the clicking sound as the dogs raced about in this growth. On the particular morning in question however the dogs looked petrified and just would not go into the beans". The circle, diameter about 10 metres, was twenty metres into the field.

An acoustic humming, buzzing or whining sound is familiar to observers of whirlwind phenomena, but effects of funnel luminosity, although noticed for some tornadoes (chiefly nocturnal events but some daytime occurrences are on record too), are unknown in devil-whirlwind contexts largely because the latter are necessarily limited to day-time visitations. In this work we shall show that acoustic, optical and electromagnetic phenomena are intrinsic characteristics of the circle-making vortices too (Chapters 4 *et seq*). The evidence will be forthcoming as the book proceeds, but firstly we consider the probable general origin of these unusual and interesting atmospheric happenings.

Chapter Three

TOPOGRAPHICAL RELIEF AND THE FORMATION
OF CIRCLE-MAKING VORTICES

All nature is but art, unknown to thee;
All chance, direction, which thou canst not see.

Alexander Pope, Essay on Man.

3.1 THE ATMOSPHERIC ORIGINS OF THE CIRCLE-MAKING VORTICES

In the first years of this investigation advances were slow because progress relied upon the chance discoveries of new circles. Not only is the phenomenon uncommon, but for obvious reasons neither place nor date could be predicted in advance. But gradually it became clear that many new sites were being found in the vicinity of hills, sometimes at or near their foot, upon their slopes, and at or beyond their head. Therefore with each new season, the totals grew because of the advantage gained by returning regularly to former sites as well as seeking new ones. Besides, from 1986 onwards aerial surveys have helped to swell the totals, while a greater public awareness has added to the feedback. These factors are sufficient to account for the rapid rise in the numbers of circles being found annually. Only when we have saturation knowledge about circle frequencies for a given large area (say, the size of southern England) might it be possible to commence looking for any time-dependent effects on rates of occurrence (such as had been optimistically attempted for ball-lightning frequencies in Holland using data for the period 1880 to 1965[18]).

Eventually the slow and patient procedure by which circle numbers have been steadily raised has borne fruit in another direction – because by visiting the best of the former circle sites frequently (sometimes daily), an increasing number of dates of formation has been established. This has meant that conditions of wind and weather can be brought into the equation with ever-improving accuracy.

The primary discovery regarding the character of circle-sites is that many *but not all* circles, and therefore their parent vortices, form in the lee of hills or escarpments. Sometimes circles appear as much as several kilometres downwind of the obstacles, especially when beyond *upslope* escarpments or massive isolated hills. In the latter case the distance away is likely to be some function of obstacle height. This relationship allows us to combine our own findings with the results of experimental, observational and theoretical research of other scientists into obstacle-related airflow and turbulence effects. On the other hand, a number of circles have been found which certainly formed to windward of, although close to, such topographical disturbances. For a few others, no prominent slopes could be discerned within a five-kilometre radius, although the ground is then usually rather undulating with perhaps obstacles more distant. Yet it cannot be gainsaid that meteorological factors not yet understood or recognized may yet combine and operate so as to produce the circumstances responsible for circles-effect vortices over open country. As this is likely to remain an unresolved issue for a considerable time, we are necessarily restricted to dealing with the evidence as it stands. We therefore commence with the lee-effect which is easiest to explain and understand (Sections 3.2 and 3.4), and afterwards consider apparent and true windward cases (Sections 3.5 to 3.6).

3.2 THE INFLUENCE OF RELIEF IN THE TRAILING-VORTEX PROCESS

Research has shown that an atmospheric disturbance or hill wave is *always present* in the airflow downwind of an obstacle, often occupying a wedge-shaped volume extending upward and outward from it. For the specific well-researched hills of quasi-conical Ailsa Craig (an island off the coast of south-west Scotland) and the massive Rock of Gibraltar, a trailing vortex system appears downwind for certain windspeeds and directions[19, 20]. This vortex may assume a horseshoe-shaped twin-roll character which is vertically or horizontally oriented or take the form of a single trailing vortex with some resemblance in style and behaviour to the better-studied aircraft wake vortices. It is probable that similar effects develop in the lee of hills and escarpments generally, and that they can interact with air columns, if well-developed, implanted in nodal situations or saddle-points typical of airflow complexities downwind of such obstacles. The geophysical vortex that leads to the circular traces in the crops, the circles effect, has its origin either in the behaviour of the saddle-point columnar vortex or more directly in the trailing vortex itself by a mechanism that has yet to be researched. Something energetic takes place to disturb the relative tranquillity of the dynamic stability of the spinning column or trailing vortex and forces a component of its energy, probably concentrated into a small volume, to follow a path that eventually leads to self-destruction at the ground or in the air. Following the suggestions of Dr John Snow, Purdue University, U.S.A., it is considered that one form of this may be vortex breakdown of a concentrated core aloft which is induced by changing external factors to start moving more or less rapidly groundwards[21].

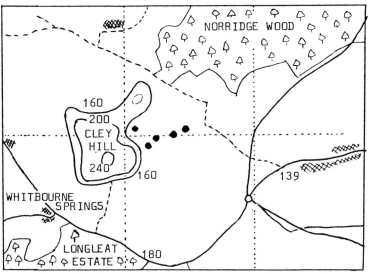

Fig.20: Cley Hill and its environs, showing the sites of known circles 1982-1985. Whitbourne Springs (cf Section 2.7) is to the south-west.

But whether or not vortex breakdown leads directly or indirectly to the circles-effect, there is certainly some sort of lee-influence operating on at least some, and perhaps many, occasions.

3.3 LEE EFFECTS AT CLEY HILL

Cley Hill is a steep-sided turf-covered knoll of chalk rising to a height of 60 metres above the cereal-fields between Warminster and Frome. The hanging woods of Longleat are just to its south and a lesser subsidiary knoll is an appendage to the hill on its northern side (Figure 20).

We have evidence of unusual effects of likely lee origin for several compass directions within a couple of kilometres of Cley Hill. Three involving atmospheric vortices with luminescent effects were described in the previous chapter. Whitbourne Springs (Section 2.7) is 300 metres south-west of the base of the hill, while the north-west part of Longleat Woods (Section 2.7) is 1½ kilometres south-east of the hill. The majority of crop circles formed by the circles effect have been found in fields to the east. The positions of all the circles known for 1982 to 1985 are indicated in Figure 20. These particular fields had none in 1986-1989.

In two instances the date of formation was sufficiently well-delimited that a westerly geostrophic wind was assignable to the event with a fair degree of probability. The quintuplet formation of 1984 exemplifies this[22]. Its formation was definitely between 1500 GMT on 21st June and 17 on 24th between which times the wind blew from between west-south-west and north-west. The evening of 21st or the night of 21st-22nd was the most likely time of formation. In the evening the wind was *light* west-north-west and the sky had good clear periods which permitted strong radiation conditions and doubtless well-stratified air, but gradually after midnight the wind backed to west-south-west and picked up progressively with the approach of a front. Our experience gained from the study of dateable circles studied in subsequent years suggests that the critical moment came when the west-south-west wind started to rise and provoked a vortical disturbance in a pre-existing stable configuration of the atmosphere. This would also appear to explain what happened south-west of Windmill Hill on 16 June 1988 when Roy Lucas observed his mist-filled vortices (cf Section 2.6)[14].

3.4 LEE EFFECTS GENERALLY

Certainly the consensus of the assembled evidence is that on at least some occasions a stably-stratified airstream seems to be a necessary pre-requisite to vortex/circle creation, and that in some manner the state of steady regular flow is abruptly modified. This can occur when the obstacle is imperfectly shaped, so that the airflow which its mass divides acquires asymmetrical components whose irregularities are felt as the separated winds re-unite on the blind side. John Heighes has described a like situation for smoke-filled vortices created downwind of an industrial chimney[23, 24].

How near or far from the obstacle do circles-effect vortices form?

Some are very close, at the foot of the hill say, or just beyond the crest, while others seem possibly linked to hills at two, three or more kilometres. In fact, there are cases where no obvious hill is in the vicinity, although the ground may undulate to a greater or lesser degree. This recalls the situation with lenticular or lee-wave clouds which are initiated by airflow disturbances introduced by irregular surface relief. Waveclouds have the property of remaining stationary for long periods downstream of parent obstacles. Of interest to us is that waveclouds can even develop over terrain that is not rugged[25].

The punchbowl-shaped concavity beneath Cheesefoot Head in Hampshire is a well-known site for observing the circles effect. Surrounded on three sides by steep slopes the punchbowl, Cheesefoot Bottom, faces north (Figure 21). For all wind directions except north the basin is subject to fluctuating winds which vary in speed and direction according to the vagaries of the geostrophic flow, itself locally modified by the complex arrangement of slopes and hills external to the punchbowl; and even northerly winds will butt against the bluff face of the steep slope. Similar three-sided sites are known elsewhere in Wessex, and doubtless many exist throughout the world, some of which are regularly planted with crops. These are the places, wherever they may be, which it is best to monitor for the circles effect.

Regular morning and evening observations at Cheesefoot by Mr P. Delgado and Mr D. Tuersley in July 1986 allowed the fixing of the time of formation of a ringed circle with sufficient precision for the result to be useful and

Fig.21: Cheesefoot Bottom, Hampshire, looking east. Enclosed on three sides, the punchbowl-shaped basin below Cheesefoot Head is open to the north. The triplet circles appeared in August 1981 (photographs by Stephen Broome).

important. The circle was undeniably absent at 10 p.m. clock time (21 GMT) in the evening of Friday 4 July, yet was sighted in twilight conditions at 3.40 the next morning[26]. Not only did these observations positively fix the time of circle creation to the night-time but it locked it into a period of overcast rainy conditions, the entire night having been damp with periods of rain and light winds chiefly from the south-west.

This circle, besides possessing an outer ring, had a contra-rotation configuration within its centre-circle bed. A similar complex system appeared at Bratton, West Wiltshire, a few days later (Figure 11). The author found it early on 13th July, within 36 hours of its creation. Although its time of formation is imperfectly known, it occurred during a wet spell from which we may say (using my local weather diary notes – I live 14 kilometres to the north-west) that it certainly formed under overcast skies and most likely under wet conditions.

The third and only other known example with internal contra-rotation happened at Childrey, Oxfordshire, during the night of 25-26 July 1986 (information kindly provided by the farmer Mr Matthews). The wind that night was south-west to west-north-west throughout, the weather of the evening cloudy, and the night overcast with rain. This was the first circle system known to us which had a radial spur issuing from the outer ring. The compass direction of the four-metre long spur was from 280 degrees (a plan is provided in Figure 38). Not only is spur-formation one of the principal wholly-unsolved mysteries, but we must also ask by what process can the airflow conduct itself in order to produce contra-rotation effects in this fashion? In view of the wet conditions experienced at or about the time these three circles appeared we ask whether the contra-rotation enigma could be linked in some way with the presence of quantities of rainwater falling through the atmosphere, and therefore through the vortex too, during the time that the vortex is grounded? The reason for this conjecture will become clearer after reading Chapters 4 and 5, for it is our thesis that the circles-effect vortex, like the vortices of whirlwinds and tornadoes, is electrically charged.

3.5 A WELL-WITNESSED CIRCLE, SEEMINGLY TO WINDWARD OF A HILL

In the previous chapter the laying out of a spiral-circle at Westbury, Wiltshire, was described (Section 2.2). The witness's lucid account poses a formidable challenge at interpretation due to the peculiarities of the circumstances attending the manner in which the circle was swept out. So until we have received a large number of eye-witness descriptions, at least as detailed as this one, we cannot say how typical this one is, but we wish to warn the reader that the circle's 'bed-making' on this occasion may not necessarily have been representative of the majority of spirally-patterned beds.

The first point concerns the cumulonimbus which was moving transversely to the hillside from north-west to south-east and had just given a shower of rain. The circle formed north-west and below the scarp, i.e. apparently on the windward side of the slope (Figure 22). However, the airflow at ground level beneath the rear section of cumulonimbus clouds is contrary to the movement of the main cloud which is always steered by the upper winds (north-west in this instance). Therefore, the local wind at the time of circle-creation would have been 'off the hill', i.e. it was blowing *from* the south-east, not *towards* the south-east. If the vortex was associated with a wake effect emanating from the hilltop, it was trailing down the slope, so that it was lying almost sideways as it tracked across the canopy of the cereal crop. Rotation in either sense would produce a line element in the manner described, but as we shall see only a vortex with cyclonic spin could produce the clockwise circle observed.

Fig.22: Looking south-east at the sloping field near Westbury where the formation of a vortex-circle was witnessed on 3 July 1982.

Without attempting to establish the nature of the vortex-supporting system in further detail we remark that the circle appeared because one end of the spinning column suddenly dug into the crop and pivoted about a point which became the middle of the circle. What had until then been a line on the crop surface was ordained to become a radius of the sector of a circle whose angle quickly grew from zero to 360 degrees (Figure 16). This instantaneous transfiguration between linear and circular states testifies unambiguously to the presence of a pivoting vortex. It recalls the action of a child's spinning top or gyroscope as it topples over and rolls around a circle. The marking out of a clockwise trace points to a cyclonic vortex because its direction of spin must have been anticlockwise (i.e. cyclonic) as viewed from above. What could have induced it to become a ground-seeking vortex?

If the origin of the vortex was the 'free' end of a hilltop trailing-vortex system, such a 'trailing end' cannot really be free. It would normally be tied to some part of the turbulent wind-structure for instance. So we suggest that by the inevitably complex vicissitudes of downdraught airflows from the shower cloud the channel of the trailing-vortex system found itself angled towards ground level. Until then dynamically satisfied, the vortex suddenly sensed, via frictional and surface interactions, the proximity of the land surface. This encouraged tilting towards the nearest boundary, i.e. the cornfield, followed by the sudden pivoting which 'freed' the vortex and allowed it to run the circle.

This is about as far as we can go for the moment in interpreting the Westbury case. Whether or not the hypothesis fully and exactly explains the scenario is not too important at this stage. What is most important is that the event happened as reported by the witness – it happened in daylight, right beneath the Salisbury Plain escarpment in what would normally be construed as a windward situation, and in a total elapsed time of some four seconds. What is more, the phenomenon was accompanied by the humming sound that is characteristic of electrical activity in ordinary whirlwinds and of electrical discharges in general, this particular case developing in the presence of an electrically-charged thundercloud. More reports, more data are what we are seeking now. We therefore eagerly await the receipt of further eye-witness accounts and, hopefully one day, instrumented observations.

3.6 WINDWARD CASES GENERALLY

The foregoing was a special case of vortex descent on the geostrophic windward side of a hill, and we saw how it could have been the local wind beneath a cumulonimbus which drew a trailing vortex, almost certainly electrically-charged, in that direction. But what are we to make of the rather considerable number of well-documented cases of vortices appearing to windward in what seem to be innocuous weather situations?

Figure 2 was taken over the fields of Bratton in August 1987. The escarpment here runs west-south-west to east-north-east. The triple set appeared on 3rd or 4th August (when the wind was 'nominally' west or west-north-west). The doubled-doublet was formed in two stages, the first pair on 28th/29th July (wind west to north-west), the second pair on 14th/15th August (wind north-west to west-south-west). The quintuplet arrived on 20th or 21st August (wind south-south-east to south-west). Only this last seems to have clearly resulted from a lee-effect. In addition, about a kilometre to the east, in the same field as the quintuplet, was a double-ringed circle. This was first seen at 10 a.m. on 8th August, having probably formed during the preceding 24 hours[27]. The wind was about west-north-west at the start of this period, and west at the end having been west-south-west for part of the night. This case is marginal, although a lee-effect is possible by the action of a vortex trailing east-north-eastwards from the scarp edge above the White Horse. But regarding the others, we must ask: did they form in truly windward conditions? Or did the wind fall very light, perhaps in the middle of the night, with subsequent complex local conditions as the wind picked up again after dawn?

This is a continuing mystery until more data are available. One really requires to monitor wind direction and wind speed at numerous positions in the vicinity of a circle while it is being made. Meanwhile in Chapter 7 we extend our inquiry in another direction and propose a novel approach by which the possibility is raised that *ionized* vortices may have the intrinsic capacity to move against the wind.

In this chapter a tentative discussion was held of some of the theoretical concepts relating to atmospheric vortices when they are in the vicinity of hills or undulating rugged land. We were concerned primarily with the experimental evidence which insists that by a means as yet to be established some *component* of an atmospheric vortex system succeeds in reaching ground level against the long-held logic that the vortex currents should be ascending ones. Moreover, we have not indicated what shapes this component may assume in the circles-effect situation, save to say that it is axi-symmetrical. Clarification of these and other points will appear in due course.

Chapter Four

INTRODUCTION TO THE PROPERTIES OF ELECTRICALLY-CHARGED VORTICES

Hear ye not the hum
Of mighty workings?

John Keats

We are now set to expand the discourse by taking note of the acoustic, optical and electrical properties of Nature's atmospheric vortices. As these are the properties of those much-studied whirlwinds which we know as tornadoes and dust-devils, it is valid to imagine that similar or related characteristics may be the natural accompaniments of the energetic aerial vortices which create the circles effect.

4.1 THE ACOUSTIC EFFECTS IMPLY ELECTRICAL DISCHARGE

For daytime eye-witnesses a notable ancillary attribute of the spinning vortex, as it lays down a crop as a spiral-centred or a star-centred circle or as it clears a circular area in a cropless field, is the sound it makes. The witness to the crop-circle at Westbury in July 1982 spoke of a coincident rustling and hissing sound[9]. The rustle came from the falling straws, and the hiss from the vortex. The witnesses at Starr Hill, also in Wiltshire, in the 1970's, spoke of a steady humming noise while the grass was being fanned into a spiral-circle. Other examples are given below, but firstly we point out that such noises are commonplace with dust-whirlwinds, and that the mighty roar which is so typical of a tornado funnel is often accompanied by a less intense but higher-pitched whining, hissing, buzzing, or humming sound. *It is significant that these sounds are acoustic noise indicative of coronal and other electrical discharge. They imply the presence and motion of electrical charges in all these natural vortices.*

4.2 THE ELECTRIC FIELDS OF DEVILS, OR ORDINARY WHIRLWINDS

The most approachable of atmospheric vortices for the experimentalist is the species of whirlwind known as the land-devil, dust-devil, or fair-weather whirlwind. These vortices are caused by the horizontal inflow of slowly-rotating air which gyrates more and more rapidly as it concentrates itself into a tubular column and rises, spinning fast, almost vertically upwards. Invisible of themselves, these vortices are detectable by dust particles and debris thus raised from the surface of the ground. The electrostatic field of this type of whirlwind vortex has been measured by Freier[28] and Crozier[29, 30] in ground-level experiments and by Bradley and Semonin[31] in airborne work flying aircraft through dust-devils. What this means for the vortex-watcher is that there is much more to the modest little whirlwind than meets the eye, because it is at one and the same time an electrostatic generator!

Crozier's first measurements were made on a fairly large dust-devil in New Mexico of diameter 20 metres and visible height 120 metres. At its closest approach of 450 metres Crozier measured the potential gradient as -61 V m^{-1}, compared with the fair-weather field of $+49$ V m^{-1} which prevailed before and after the event. Freier, in the Sahara, found -450 V m^{-1} for a devil passing at a distance of 30 metres. Interestingly, the field/time relationship in both cases could be approximated to that of an equivalent vertical dipole. A surprisingly high space-charge density was indicated in Crozier's work which he ascribed to the heavy loading with large dust particles of the surface air drawn into the cylindrical sheath of the vortex. In his later paper[30] Crozier reported similar data for seventeen dust-devils; some had even higher electric field strengths (cf Section 7.7.)

The intrinsic ability of fast-spinning heat-induced vortices in the lower atmosphere to acquire electrostatic fields is of fundamental importance. It suggests that dust devils if they could occur at night would have self-luminous walls! Unfortunately, their development is restricted to the super-adiabatic conditions of the heat of the day so their capacity to emit light has never been noticed, but our circle-making vortices are not so limited to daytime production, and neither are tornado funnel clouds some of which at night-time have paraded their luminescent features before large numbers of eye-witnesses, a few with cameras (as at Toledo, U.S.A. in 1965 and Huntsville in 1974).

The charge carriers inside dust-devils appear to be negative charges carried on the aerosol particles which are raised from the ground by the winds of the vortex. Because in normal fair-weather conditions there is a net negative charge on the surface of the earth, this can explain how a negative potential gradient can commence and grow, and overwhelm the positive fair-weather field. Eventually one deduces that the negative space-charge in the whirling air increases so much that a corresponding positive charge is induced upon the ground, after which fresh dust carries positive instead of negative charge into the column – hence the apparent dipole structure[32].

For the circles-effect vortex, electrostatic charges made airborne by disturbed dust particles may be a secondary effect at best, only happening when a descending vortex approaches a dry crop on dusty ground. Instead, the main effect is more likely to result from the energetic spin regime originating at higher altitudes. Indeed, what we are proposing is that *the dynamics of ion and electron assemblies are the significant factor in the circles-effect problem,* and that the fast-spinning vortices whose windfields carve the circles on the ground are possibly constituted of *a self-luminous low-density plasma,* whose electrical, optical and acoustic effects originate from simple discharge recombination processes. However, before dealing with the ever-mounting evidence in favour of this unique discovery, it is advantageous to review the electrical properties of tornadoes.

4.3 SOME OF THE KNOWN ELECTRICAL PROPERTIES OF TORNADO VORTICES

Despite the difficulty and danger of approaching tornadoes with test instruments much observational and deductive evidence has been accumulated regarding the electrical characteristics of some well-observed very strong tornadoes. In summarizing the evidence Vonnegut has included many historical as well as modern examples in his review[33].

The electrification of clouds is the province not only of the obvious thunderstorm but indeed of all convective clouds. What Vonnegut stressed firmly is that lightning and other electrical effects are so much more intense in the so-called 'prester' variety of tornadic storm than for other tornadoes and non-tornadic thunderstorms. (By reviving the old word 'prester' Vonnegut meant the 'fiery whirlwind' which descends in the form of a pillar of fire – a

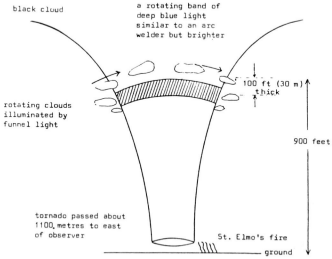

Fig.23: Sketch of tornado with bright luminous band or ring, seen at Blackwell, Oklahoma (after Montgomery, ref. 34). This tornado produced radio-frequency sferics typical of a pulse-generator.

metaphorical allusion to its luminosity). Dr. Vonnegut, in noting that intense electrical activity precedes and follows the appearance of the funnel, took the position that the electrification begets the prester tornado. Not only is the cloud-to-cloud and cloud-to-ground lightning more intense and incessant in prester tornadoes but the cylindrical walls of the funnels when viewed from nearby, or from beneath, are seen to be ablaze with light, resembling a self-illuminated tube. The Blackwell (Oklahoma) tornado was remarkable for its waist-like rotating band of blue light, said to be comparable in hue to an arc welder but brighter[34]. Figure 23 has been prepared after Montgomery's original.

French and English tornadoes have likewise been reported to display dramatic effects involving column luminosity, coloured lightning, and coloured balls of fire sometimes of enormous size. Several French accounts exist of tornadoes tossing out balls of light from near their lower ends, while some English accounts refer similarly to red balls or sparks. Referring to this phenomenon the great French astronomer Camille Flammarion wrote last century that tornadoes eject ball lightning 'like hens lay eggs'. This connection between spinning tornadoes and some occurrences of ball lightning is encouraging for our general idea of a spinning low-density air plasma as being the key to the circles effect.

Good British tornadoes to cite are Egremont (Cumbria) 1960 and Newbottle (Northants) 1872, so we take a look at these. On 17 January 1960 a nocturnal tornado passed through Egremont, Cumbria, with T5 intensity on the TORRO scale, removing roofs in its passage and shifting a prefabricated house 50 feet. Mr John Braithwaite watching through his bedroom window saw the tornado coming straight for the house and said it looked like 'a great ball of fire'[35]. The Newbottle tornado of 30 November 1872 was investigated by Beesley[36] from whose report we judge its strength to be T4. It was reported that four witnesses "who saw it from different points . . . agree they heard a whizzing, roaring sound like a passing train, which attracted their attention, and then saw a huge revolving ball of fire travelling from six to eight feet off the ground. The smoke was whizzing round and rising high into the air, and a blast of wind accompanied it, carrying a cloud of branches along and destroying everything in its way". Other witnesses reported red sparks issuing from it.

Nocturnal and daytime sightings in which part of a tornado column was described as a 'ball of fire' can be cited for Holkham, Norfolk (September 1741), and Pendeen, Cornwall (25 November 1938). A waterspout off the Needles in May 1944 had a 'bright red fire burning inside and throwing out quite big red sparks'. The 'sparks' were perhaps small globes of lightning, akin to the balls of lightning sometimes witnessed in the vicinity of the base of tornado funnels or even issuing from them. Michael Rowe mentions others including a luminous Irish tornado having a 'tower of fire' in the year 1054 at Rosdalla[37].

4.4 SFERICS AND THEIR GENERATION

Besides the visual evidence cited by Vonnegut[33], and the later spectacle filmed and photographed at Huntsville, Alabama, in April 1974[38], there is the confirmation of increased radio-frequency sferics (a word coined from 'atmospherics') in tornado-producing storms compared with non-tornadic storms. The sferics produced by the tornado's electrical charges not only upset radio and aircraft communications over long distances but disrupt television reception as well. Indeed stories are plentiful in which householders ascertain that their television is suffering from severe interference or is going dead, and then, on looking outside, they catch sight of a tornado bearing down on the neighbourhood. Well, an almost analagous story exists for the circle-producing vortex! This is the Japanese event of 9 August 1986 referred to in Chapter 1 (Section 1.6) in which a sudden blast scored a three-metre diameter radial-type circle into the mud of a garden pond, having announced its arrival by a synchronous bright light and such great interference on a television receiver that the set had to be switched off.

In fact sferic detection and monitoring has long been a method for tracking tornadoes as it has for thunderstorms[39]. A cloud-to-ground lightning stroke radiates radio-wave energy most intensely at around 10^4 Hz. H. L. Jones reported that sferics on the low-frequency 10^4 Hz waveband are much more intense in a tornado-producing cloud than those from ordinary thunderstorms, and that the sferics' frequencies move to higher values as the tornado strengthens. A significant correlation has been established between the number of sferics flashes at 150 kHz and tornado occurrence and their intensity.

This flashing rate or pulse repetition rate has even been seen visually, the first recorded occasion being 25 May 1955 at Blackwell, Oklahoma. This tornado was tracked and watched from the Stillwater Tornado Laboratory using a 150 kHz direction finder as it passed 20-25 kilometres to the west[40] Observers noticed "an odd flashing of a patch of illumination in the top section of the thundercloud, a flashing that appeared as a circular patch of light on the side of the cloud structure between the observer and the centre of action where the electrical activity appeared to be. At that time these patches of light appeared as circular patches of pale blue illumination for an estimated time of two seconds; this circular area would then become dark for another estimated period of two seconds, and again would reappear". The staff of the Tornado Laboratory concluded that the electrical activity on the oscilloscope of the direction finder was emitted by the flashing, pulsed light high in the cloud, the same place as the precipitation echo seen on radar associated with the tornado funnel. As Dr Jones remarked, this was Nature's own 'tornado pulse-generator.

The ability of tornado-vortex systems to generate electrical activity on such a scale, and pulsed activity at that, is what attracts our attention. On the basis of evidence yet to be deliberated (Chapter 6), electrical-generating counterparts are to be inferred for the circles-effect vortex, but on a lesser scale. Other matters involving electrification commonly associated with tornadoes are corona discharges (St Elmo's fire) which develop just ahead of the tubular funnel, and their subsequent consequences for bystanders (raised hair, tingling sensations, sounds of crackling or hissing etc). In addition, electrical breakdown accounts for the commonly-smelt 'sulphurous'-type odours arising from the production of ozone and nitrogen oxides.

The high space-density of the electrical discharges can also be the origin of hot or warm air currents and the physical sensations of heat occasionally reported in the vicinity of tornado vortices. They are likely to be the source of the scorching or dessication of vegetation found along some tornado paths, and may cause the breathing difficulties reported by some bystanders caught in the vortex.

4.5 THE ELECTRICALLY-CHARGED VORTEX WHICH MAKES THE CIRCLES

Having summarized the properties which the more familiar natural atmospheric vortices possess, we now investigate to what extent electrical and magnetic effects can develop in the forced-wind vortices which lead to the crop circles.

Our proposal is that the wind-shear and the localized vorticity which lead to columnar and breakdown vortices of the type introduced in Chapter 3 are the *fons et origo* of the electrified vortices at the heart of the effect. These vortices may be plasma vortices, constituted of the familiar atmospheric materials of air and water vapour but in which an effective percentage of atoms and molecules have become charged through electron loss and ionization. Or they may possess more of an electrostatic character, by analogy with the devil-whirlwind, in which dust and other particles are the carriers of both negative and positive ions.

The essential feature is a rapidly spinning vortex which by creating and separating the charges promotes intense electric and magnetic fields accompanied by light-producing and sound-producing discharges. At the same time the radio-frequency fields are responsible for a number of subsidiary effects as we see below. Just as the vortex when off-the-ground can have a long life in which the mechanical energy for its spin is continually fed into the system along the length of the column, so can its electrical energy be sustained for comparatively long periods by the same means. Above threshold levels enough charges are present and concentrated by the gyrating wind as to produce identifiable acoustic, optical and other electromagnetic effects. But when the phenomenon has come to an end, little evidence remains for the investigator to examine unless he chances upon the precious ground-trace patterns which constitute the 'circles effect'. The power of the circles effect as an analytical tool is then manifest. By examining the traces we gather data on their absent creators.

Let us consider the chief properties of these vortices, and follow and predict some of their consequences.

4.6 SOME OF THE EVIDENCE FOR DESCENDING LUMINOUS VORTICES

We commence by looking at case-histories involving luminous vortices for which evidence of circular ground traces is beyond dispute.

Firstly there is the St Souplet case, from the Department du Nord (France), in which a three-metre circle was flattened into a bed of spinach one night in 1963 or 1964 (Figure 24). The principal witness was awakened by 'a violent report at which moment she noticed a huge red light taking off from her garden'; the next-door neighbour was wakened as well[41]. In the context of mysterious lights such as this one the colours most frequently noted are, besides white, orange and red.

This account was sent to me in 1985 by a French correspondent, M. Jean Sider, as one example of the few known circles-effect cases for that country. It was timely, for it set me firmly along the final trail of deduction as regards the electromagnetic character of the circle-making vortices, reinforcing as it did my pre-existing knowledge concerning the electrodynamics of natural vortices. In 1983 I had already wondered whether the miniscule ring, a few centimetres wide but a hundred metres long which linked the Bratton quintuplet satellites (referred to in Sections 1.1, 1.8), might be an 'ion race' rather than a surveyor's footpath, and in 1985 came published photographs from the quintuplet at Goodworth Clatford (July 1985) which showed the same thing. And now there was the St Souplet crop-circle, created

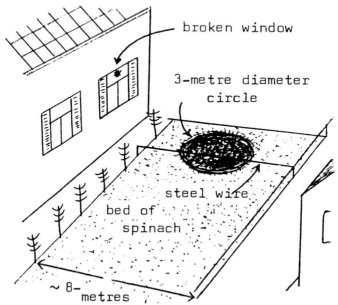

Fig.24: Circle in a crop of spinach at St. Souplet, in the north of France, whose formation was accompanied by a loud report and a strongly-glowing red light.

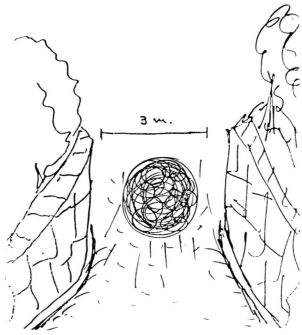

Fig.25: Representation of a spinning ball of light which made
the noise of a whirlwind, seen at Malcata, Portugal
(forwarded to the author by V.-J. Ballester Olmos).

unambiguously at the time of optical and acoustic effects. Surely, the circles-effect vortex must consist of ionized air, just like its relatives in the whirlwind-tornado family, because this would mean that its luminous, sound, and spin properties could fully explain the St Souplet sighting.

At almost the same time a Spanish correspondent (Sr V.-J. Ballester Olmos) sent me eight Iberian items of remarkable atmospheric phenomena for appraisal because they involved vortices. Some were readily explained with reference to dust-devils and tornadoes but four were quite puzzling. No crop circles were associated with them, but one (from Portugal, dated about August 1935), which was described in the report as a self-illuminated spinning wind with the noise of a 'vento di ciclone' which hovered at ground level, I recognised as a likely nocturnal vortex of the 'circles effect' type with marked ball-lightning characteristics (Figure 25). But its lifetime and size (it was nearly three metres in diameter) precluded ball lightning. Could the circles-effect vortex be the explanation for the numerous puzzling incidents reported over the years of big balls of light capable of lasting for minutes on end? Unexceptional though the illustration is, it is reproduced just because it is so typical of many others, with its luminosity, its roundness, its spin, and its whirlwind noise. Also, its known position in a lane enabled its size to be fairly exactly estimated without exaggeration.

Two of the Spanish cases were similar to the Portuguese one. The first (for 12 August 1975) was a luminous daytime instance of a spinning wind-vortex, *una ráfaga de aire en torbellino luminoso*. Just as interesting was a well-documented case for 26 March 1982 from Pontevedra, Spain, in which subsequent to hearing a noise like an explosion a phenomenon said to resemble a whirlwind was seen scouring an area of land of its movable vegetation and stones. The description was clear in implying a steady *downward* action. Reading it made me recall the peculiar story from Canada which I had seen years earlier when working on the TORRO tornado/whirlwind data-bank. This is the stone-clearing incident in Ontario, 1880, introduced in Section 1.7[5]. It was a year later (1986) that I learnt of what may have been a similar happening in the south of Wiltshire. At Charlton in the middle of July 1963 a hollow was found at the edge of a potato field adjacent to barley. Contemporary investigations were inconclusive but I could now interpret the occurrence as the result of a downblast so severe that instead of the usual circle a shallow crater was hollowed into the wet soil and the potatoes were cast far aside. The date of the happening was unknown, except to say that if it was 10th July that was when a policeman saw an orange ball of light which vanished near or at the same field. A similar case with scorching happened in a field of brussels sprouts in 1966 near Sharnbrook, Bedfordshire.

Many other pertinent examples enjoining lights and vortices have been assembled and will be published elsewhere. So to keep the narrative short we leap past the significant 'electromagnetic' developments which arose from the arrival of the ringed spiral-circles in 1986, the mixed-rotations of the quintuplets in 1987, and the Silbury Hill pipe-luminescence sighting of July 1988 to pause at September 1988 when a further clue linking the electromagnetic-vortex theory to the circles effect was added to the earlier and intervening ones. From Fornham All Saints in Suffolk came a report that on 11 September a 13-metre circle was found in a field of sugarbeet at the exact spot where the previous evening a strong bright light had 'come down like a bullet' and hovered there. When the circle was re-examined several days later the damaged sugarbeet was found to be discoloured, wilting and no longer healthy. And the month before I had been informed by Clive Potter of a midnight sighting on 4th August 1988 in the Midlands of 'a large glowing mass about 30 feet across on the edge of the road. It was a large cloud with a red pulsating light within it and it was lying on top of the hedge, before shooting off at great speed'. This was in Staffordshire at Seven Springs, Colwich, Rugeley. About three-and-a-half metres of the hedge were slightly damaged; a thorough inspection was made by David Reynolds on behalf of CERES. Was this happening a species of vortex pulse-generator at work?

These various sightings powerfully combine the production of circular damage patterns with the descent of spinning-wind systems which at night-time are self-luminous. Yet there are additional effects which add their crucial weight. Let us begin with the luminescent channel or conducting pipe.

4.7 THE SELF-LUMINOUS PIPE

In July 1988 a wheatfield south of Silbury Hill was the scene of three independent visitations by descending vortices during which no less than 13 circles were formed (cf Figure 41). The first event produced a quintuplet, found the morning of 15th July alongside the busy A4 trunk road (Figure 26). The *Marlborough Times* carried a report which mentioned that a witness late on the 13th while driving along the Kennet Avenue from Avebury had seen "a constant beam of white light" which "stretched from the clouds to the ground" near Silbury Hill. A female correspondent informed me that the lady-witness had described the light source within the cloudbase as oval-shaped and that the beam was angled in the general direction of the area where the circles were later found. Speaking later with the witness I learnt that the beam was pencil-shaped and *hollow;* in other words, it was not a beam at all but a pipe or tube *emitting its own light.* This makes it look like a case of an angled columnar vortex illuminated by a discharge current, in which the pipe served to provide a conducting path between cloud and earth. The source of the hollow shaft of light was a huge volume of illuminated cloud (the size of a football pitch) which was glowing within the cloud-mass a little to the north of Silbury. The cloud was obviously electrified, so it seemed to me that the pipe could have been channelling an electron leakage from cloud to ground, probably as a direct-current discharge.

Fig.26: Quintuplet set of circles which appeared close to Silbury Hill on 15 July 1988. A second set of five arrived eleven days later, and four days after that a further three (compare with Figure 41).

R.A.F. Lyneham kindly supplied the relevant weather information for Lyneham some ten kilometres to the west-north-west. The wind being light west-north-west the cloud details for Lyneham for 2145 GMT approximate to those for Silbury at the time of observation which the witness specified as 2213 GMT (this time interval allows for the effect of a force 4 wind at cloud-level). Cloud base was 4000 ft above ground level, and the sky five-eighths covered. The witness explained that the light shaft was angled at about 45 degrees as seen from the start of Kennet Avenue at Avebury which implies that the light was directed at a field about 4000 ft or 1250 metres to the south-east or east-south-east. This seems too far away for it to be the 'quintuplet field' but it could have been the field north-east of West Kennet long barrow which was later found to have a good single circle in it and was photographed from the air.

Additional details about the rest of the investigation, and the location of the circles (including the single circle) are being published elsewhere. Suffice it to say that other examples of self-illuminated atmospheric tubes are to be found in the scientific literature (the Toledo twin tornadoes photographed by Weyer and discussed by Vonnegut and Weyer (1966) for instance[43], and the Japanese luminous-tube case at Tomakomai, Hokkaido), and that it is our proposal that tubes like the one at Silbury are the visible representation of part of the primary columnar vortex along which a concentrated ionized-vortex or its separately-projected constituents may travel. We shall find in Chapter 5, Section 5.6, crop-damage evidence of another sort which may offer further proof of the angled-tube phenomenon.

The mystery of the circles effect has broadened substantially since we began this inquiry, having drawn into its orbit coincident optical and acoustic phenomena associated with air in an electrically-activated state. Further circumstantial evidence is provided by case-studies in which electrical properties emanating from the vortex appear to affect automobile performance too, but discussion of this is deferred until Chapter 6. First we study the effect that considerations of the electrically-charged state have on our columnar vortex model.

Chapter Five

ELECTRICAL-DISCHARGE VORTICES AND GLOBES

Truth is the golden girdle of the globe.

William Cowper

5.1 INTRODUCTION TO THE MAIN IDEAS

The assembled evidence of the preceding chapters despite its variety and complexity can be explained by a single phenomenon: a spinning mass of air which has accumulated a significant fraction of electrically-charged matter, and whose quantity is maintained by the channelling or piping in of a fresh supply of ions which replace losses by discharge and leakage. As we shall see in the course of this chapter, the balance of evidence currently available (headed by the effects arising from radio-frequency and pulsed electromagnetic waves) suggests that the spinning wind has entered the ionized state known as plasma, and that the vortices are or become plasma balls akin to ball lightning in appearance except that they are much bigger and longer-lived.

It is deduced that the external behaviour and therefore the observed features of this plasma are dominated by the dynamics of its principal attributes, (1) the spinning motion of its constituents, and (2) the electromagnetic and recombination properties of its moving charges.

The first of these characterizes the range of permissible shapes. The gyrations account for a transverse circular symmetry with respect to the principal axis, and ultimately for the circular-symmetric patterns cut into crops and fields. A spinning vortex may assume any form ranging from spherical through ellipsoidal to conical and cylindrical. In fact, the dictionary definition of a vortex is simply 'a rapid movement of particles of matter about an axis'. But when the constituents of the vortex differ from the medium in which they are spinning a kind of surface tension may be envisaged for the surface boundary, whose action is to draw the plasma into a sphere by seeking to minimize the total surface area. Therefore although the spinning wind may be set going in the shape of a funnel or cylinder or sheath, then as the ionization content intensifies the naissant plasmoid tends to adopt a spherical form in the absence of other constraints.

This hypothesis answers for the large number of low-level globular light forms reported in the scientific literature and the popular press as ball lightning, balls of light, and 'unidentified flying objects' etc. Rapid translation and simultaneous spin would tend to distort such forms, giving rise to non-globular shapes like 'cigars', ellipsoids, and, for very high spin rates, strongly-flattened forms that appear discoidal. Although our plasma-vortex hypothesis may prove to be not entirely correct when more detailed studies have been completed and very many more facts have been gathered, we believe that it points in generally the right direction. The urgent need is for more data at all levels, but above all there is a requirement for well-instrumented sightings. For it must be admitted that despite the number of years that have passed, we are still in the pioneering epoch of circle and vortex study and are having to base deductions on a limited and insufficient amount of material.

Charge recombination or discharge produces light which is sometimes coloured, red and orange being quite common; it also generates the buzzing, whining or humming sounds which are so typical of corona discharge.

The movement of charge creates magnetic fields and forces. Indications are plentiful that the fields are pulsed. Their radio-frequency fields produce the sferics (atmospherics) which are detected by radio, television and radar, besides sometimes visible effects seen as fluctuations in the optical range. Magnetic fields, if intense enough, might be expected to interfere with watch and compass movements, and just possibly with motor-car performance, but in this matter laboratory experiments on vehicular electrical systems have been performed up to 20 000 Oersteds to no avail[44]. It is more likely instead that where car electrical and ignition systems are disrupted (Sections 6.4 – 6.6) this is due either to an ionization leakage-flow from the plasma vortex, or to charges induced thereby. Corona discharges certainly explain cases of eye-witnesses having their hair stand on end, or suffering medically in various ways from ionization exposure. For some tornadoes unusual heating effects which lead to dessication of vegetation, or are sensed by the body, have been noted. This would be the result of recombination processes within the intense charge-circulation heating the air column, and at the same time illuminating the entire columnar vortex with a form of lightning discharge. There is no reason why this should not apply to non-tornadic situations too, particularly in view of the proven violence of the circles-effect vortex.

5.2 A LONGER-LIVED FORM OF BALL LIGHTNING

In practice, the physical character of the supposed vortex plasma probably hardly differs from the plasma sometimes conjectured for ball lightning, although considerable controversy still surrounds the constitution of the latter after one and a half centuries of animated discussion. Even the reality of ball lightning is disputed by some researchers, largely on the grounds that the theoretical difficulties continue to be intractable, but this is to ignore a sizeable aggregation of visual proof adduced by a large body of trustworthy witnesses some of whom are scientists.

The chief problem with the widely-known type of ball lightning, in the way that the phenomenon is conventionally understood, is how to justify theoretically the stability of the ball. For if the ball is self-consuming from the moment of its creation under thunderstorm conditions, ball-lightning lifetimes exceeding one or two seconds are reckoned impossible while times approaching one second at best are the usual result of theoretical work. P. Kapitsa's ingenious theory to improve on this relies on the continuance of a steady microwave input, but critics wonder whether enough ultrahigh-frequency radiation ever develops in thunderstorm conditions to support such a process[45].

Be that as it may, with our plasma vortex – the postulated creator of *the crop circles whose existence is at any rate beyond question on account of the traces* – although the times taken to mark out the circles are believed to be short (less than 10 seconds), longer lifetimes overall are implied by the assembled corpus of observational evidence for the plasma. In fact, lifetimes exceeding a minute or two, and sometimes approaching half-an-hour, may then be possible. This presents *no* problem for us, for maintenance of the process is assured by a continuous input piped along the conducting funnel or column, which thus replaces charges steadily lost through recombination and leakage. Descriptions of fairly long-lived plasma-like effects abound in the literature, but until now their existence has been largely disregarded through prejudiced insistence that long-lived 'ball-lightning' was not possible. *Yet not only do we have undisputed proof that such vortices form in the free atmosphere, even to the extent of being fairly common where rugged terrain plays any role, but we have a ready answer as to their persistence for periods lasting for many tens of seconds if not even many tens of minutes or more.*

5.3 SOME QUALITIES OF THE VORTEX

To begin with, we may suppose that the vortex owes its origin, directly or indirectly to topographical and airflow factors (windspeed, direction, and character of turbulent flow subsequent to possibly well-stratified airflow conditions). But the qualities of the resultant plasma (colour, space-charge density, recombination rate, noise) besides depending upon its internal energy level may depend upon additional factors like the thermo-hygrometrical properties of the air, its dust content, and a state of the atmosphere conducive to charge induction and maintenance.

For example in humid conditions the considerable quantities of water vapour present may undergo ionization in the vicinity of recombining ions, and as the temperature rises dissociation of water vapour into hydrogen and oxygen set in increasingly. A raising of the temperature not only extends the lifetime of the vortex by cascading the ionization, but the heating effect could

Fig.27: The skimming of a crop of barley by circles-effect vortices at Bratton, August 1987. No perfectly sharp edges, no fully-flattened beds, but obvious impressions all the same.

draw in additional air and encourage a 'landed' or hovering vortex to take off again and return up the column whence it came.

To be sure, there is a need to explain the puzzling observation that the stalks and plants inside some circles are not flattened hard to the ground but have been only lightly touched. Indeed in a few cases the crop seems merely to have been *skimmed,* as if by a hovering plasmoid which brushed only the surface.

Examples are reproduced in Figures 27 and 28. One of these is the large oval circle and its lesser companions formed at Bratton at the start of August 1987 in the wheatfield beneath the White Horse. The second is the double-ringed circle on Charity Down south of Goodworth Clatford, Hampshire, 1988. Others included the single-ringed circle at Bratton 1986, and the triple circles triangularly-disposed, seen at Corhampton and Cheesefoot in 1988.

As regards colour it is notable how frequently the colour red figures in reports of luminous phenomena that could be plasma, perhaps similar to ball lightning. Red is the colour in the emission spectrum of nitrogen, the dominant gas in our atmosphere, and accompanies the discharge process as nitrogen molecules fall back from excited energy states. A bluish-white light is seen instead if nitrogen is energized to even higher levels.

5.4 RINGED SYSTEMS

The singly-ringed circles are marked by the property that the direction of

Fig.28: Arcs of the double-ringer on Charity Down, south of Goodworth Clatford, Hampshire, June 1988. The weakness of the impressions contrasts with the strength of those shown by the photographs in Figures 9 and 10 which relate to another Hampshire double-ringed system formed a week earlier.

rotation of the ring is quite often opposite in direction to that of the inner circle when the latter is plain or uni-directional (Figure 29).

A problem is that, whereas rotation which surrounds stationary air is a stable configuration, a ring of stationary air surrounding rotating air is unstable. The reason for the counter-rotating sheath is obscure; it will require observational evidence, preferably recorded on video film, of the chronological development sequence in order to advance the solution. One possibility that we wish to propose is that the charge flow within the inner vortex-circle induces a charge-flow of opposite sign beyond the perimeter; motion as a counterflowing current would naturally follow, and we have the ion race-track as mentioned earlier. If correct, the inner circle comes first, and the ring follows when the field strength associated with the circle has become large enough to induce the ionized ring-current. This would explain the observation that it is mostly the bigger circles which have rings.

In fact, a comparable mystery is posed by the common waterspout in which the wall of the outer sheath is extremely thin. This sheath is a visual demonstration, about which there can be no dispute, of an exceptional confinement of particle-flow to a very narrow region. If the thinness of the waterspout sheath was not such a well-attested sight, it might be deemed an unlikely happening, or even classed as impossible. Yet this age-old and equally-demanding problem has yet to be explained satisfactorily. Perhaps the

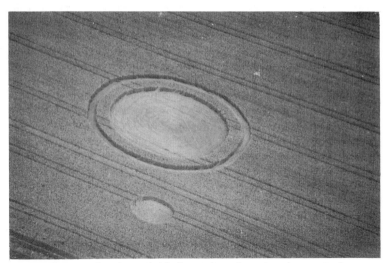

Fig.29: This ringed circle in a field of rye is from the Winterbourne Stoke group
shown in Figure 1. The internal clockwise circle is surrounded by a ring
in which the crop is laid uniformly anticlockwise.

Fig.30: Double-ringed circle at Bratton, photographed from the air and
the ground.

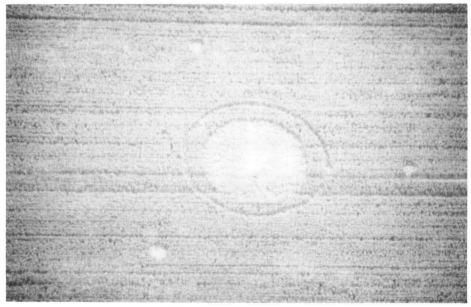

Fig.31: The ringed circle with triple satellites which formed between Oadby and Stoughton, Leicestershire, in June 1988, the only known circumstance of this formation.

solutions to the two problems are related, the sheathed regions of the waterspout being charged as well. We can at any rate cite cases of waterspout self-illumination noted at night or under poor conditions of daylight to sustain this proposal (cf Section 4.3).

The crop-circle problem is augmented further with the double-ringed systems (Figure 9 and 30), because we then find two seemingly unstable layers of air sandwiched between two stable cylindrical rotating layers, all with a common axis. It is noteworthy that the rings spin in opposite senses, and that sightings of waterspouts alike include twin-walled systems. Our explanation for this mystery comes further on.

5.5 MULTI-SET SYSTEMS

If charge induction is part of the manifestation of this phenomenon, it may account for the appearance of distant or proximal satellite systems in the tri-symmetric and quadri-symmetric sets shown in Figures 2, 3, 26, 31, 32. Similarly, the in-line triplets (Figures 2, 3, 21) may result from bi-partite symmetry conditions of a standing-wave phenomenon.

An induction effect may be the consequence of electromagnetic-wave interference resulting in antinodal extrema at the satellite positions, thus leading to secondary rotating plasmas at these locations. Over fifty years ago it was found experimentally that an ionized gas will resonate to and absorb electromagnetic waves of the appropriate frequency, and that the energy

Fig.32: Quintuplet on Beckhampton Down, south of the village, July 1988. The central circle was
      16 metres diameter, and the distance between centres of opposite satellites an enormous 83
      metres for one pair and 78 metres for the other. The quintuplets at nearby Silbury Hill
      were even bigger.

continues to be absorbed until a moment is reached when a cascade of
ionization results. If this happens as part of the circles-effect, the satellite
positions become suddenly energized in a brief explosion of activity. We
suggest that the ions are fed into the satellites along a narrow ring, a race-track
or 'ion race', which we know by photography and site inspection interlinks
them (Figure 3, row D, set 3).

The first example demonstrating this was noted at Bratton in 1983 in
association with the first-known quintuplet circle set (Figure 33). It must not
be supposed that the arcs were made by someone walking in the field as one
might hastily suspect. It is a genuine effect that is usually very hard to
photograph from the ground. Certainly, the habitual faintness of this ring is
extraordinary in itself and points to some exceptional process at work. The
straws have, as ever, been pushed over by air motion, i.e. the movement of air
molecules, but the acute narrowness of the rings (sometimes not many
centimetres) implies that some force other than a pressure gradient has
displaced the air. No better suggestion seems possible than that this force is the
electromagnetic interaction of ionized particles operating within a sheath, and
that it is their highly-localized motion that pushes against the straws. Another
good example of this effect joining the four satellites of a quintuplet appeared
south of Goodworth Clatford on Charity Down in July 1985. It was this
second appearance that convinced me that an ionized wind could be involved,
and that further, more prominent, examples are to be expected in the future.

Fig.33: Quintuplet at Bratton, July 1983, photographed by Christopher Woods, *Daily Express*, London. This was the first occasion known to us of a quintuplet formation, and the first time that the narrow ring linking the four satellite circles was seen. It is believed that this ring, which the author suspects to be an 'ion race', is generated by electromagnetic induction from intense currents circulating in the main circle. The additional lines are tracks made by visitors to the circles. c C. Woods and *Daily Express*.

One may logically propose that whereas the circulation of ions takes place in the narrow annulus, the ions congregate at the four satellite positions because these are Kapitsa-type anti-nodal sites. The narrow ring arises from electromagnetic forces, and so do the satellite circles. Notwithstanding this, the faint ring is not always seen despite the prominence or hugeness of satellite circles, possibly because on these other occasions the ions are concentrated into such a sufficiently narrow annulus that they can reinforce one another to act as crop-flattening agents.

We may consequently view the minor vortex-plasmas as satellites in time as well as space, the crop at these sites as in the rings (discussed further below) being pushed over by an electromagnetic wind. If this is correct, the effect originates in the radio-frequency field of the primary vortex, which means that its charges are likely to be an ionized plasma rather than an assembly of electrostatic charges. In short, we deduce that the main circle is formed first, and that, if and when its electromagnetic field becomes intense enough, rings and satellites appear secondarily. In this connection one should note that the central circles or quintuplet systems are always quite large in diameter, above ten or eleven metres as a rule.

As for the directions of rotation displayed by the straws lying in the satellite circles of quintuplet systems (both senses of spin are found), these may correspond to or be influenced by the net sign of the ionic charge carriers in addition to external airflow factors. In one notable case involving an in-line triplet (at Bratton 1987) the flow direction of the southernmost circle had a very muddled look about it, due it seems to an initially wholly clockwise motion being supplanted by a total movement anticlockwise. Its neighbours were normal uncomplicated circles bedded clockwise. A detailed treatment of matters like these, with photographs, will be explored elsewhere.

An eyewitness sighting of a quintuplet set of circles is urgently needed to establish the formation sequence. The Clapham/Findon set of 1985 on land at Tolmare Farm in Sussex (29 June) came close to being witnessed. A cloud of hazy mist rising from the central circle was said to resemble 'a series of fountains' according to its finders Mr K. Johnson and Mr M. Moyer. This statement suggests the men came across the site right at the end of its formation sequence. The condensation of mist reminds us of the Avebury vortex sightings of Mr Lucas (Section 2.6). As no condensation mist was noted for the satellite circles, this may support the proposal that their creation was chronologically subsidiary to the middle circle and was the result of an electromagnetic wind circulating at a lower speed which was insufficient to trigger the condensation process. Formed after dawn in the brightness of daylight (0450 GMT) no associated luminescence was noted. On the other hand, the Bishop Fonthill (Wiltshire) quintuplet event of 1985 may have formed at night-time because a resident who lives within view of the site witnessed in the middle of the night a single strong bright light above the field where the circles were found the following morning (20 July) at 06 GMT.

Finally for this section, we mention an example of a circle with plain uninterrupted ring and, well beyond it at a much greater radius, four satellites at 90-degree locations (Longwood Estate, Hampshire, August 1986 – see Figure 3, row D, set 2). This is a composite constituted of a simple ringed circle and the four satellites of a quintuplet. If there had been another ring interlinking satellites and a few additional concentric rings as well, one might have wondered whether this would constitute an optimum situation for the complexity of the circles effect in a single system, in which case most other known systems would be subset derivatives.

5.6 LABORATORY SIMULATIONS OF PLASMA-BALL PRODUCTION

Plasma-ball production by the concentrated focussing of electromagnetic waves has been successfully accomplished by Powell and Finkelstein in the laboratory[47]. Plasma balls, presumed to relate to the ball-lightning problem, persisted for half-a-second or a little more after switch-off. The triumph of these scientists has been taken by some theoreticians to exhibit the practicability of Kapitsa's ideas, serving as it does to take the theory from a mathematical abstraction to experimental fulfilment in the real world. The chief difficulty with respect to Kapitsa's theory is whether microwaves of sufficiently high frequency and strength can occur in thunderstorms. Powell and Finkelstein postulate that an externally-applied non-linear d.c. electric field could be involved in sustaining the ball lightning and hence its radio-frequency discharges, but they conclude that much more detailed theoretical and experimental work is needed.

We regard the success of the Powell-Finkelstein experiment as applying in principle to our own low-density plasma balls. It is the end result which is important (i.e. the plasma ball), not the process used (their experimental method is not the one that applies in nature) – but whether the electric-field intensities are sufficiently great in the extra-laboratorial world is another question. Nevertheless, it might be thought on the evidence of the sightings of luminescent tubes of great length (Section 4.7) and for other reasons, that fields of the right type do at least occur naturally. The proposed vortex-tube may effectively channel an electron leakage current from cloud to plasmoid and to the ground. By this means, the columnar vortex or trailing vortex that we imagine to be the mechanism behind the whole process could gather charge from a volume many thousands of times greater than that of the plasma vortex-ball, and thereby account for an extraordinary ball-of-light longevity in contrast to the accustomed brevity of ball-lightning.

5.7 SINGLE RINGS NOT ENCLOSING CIRCLES

Nothing is known observationally about the sequence in which the crop is laid down in typical plain circles, nor in the special cases of ringed or complex circles. It is thought that the splendid well-witnessed case, at Westbury in July 1982 which involved a 'fan-opening' effect, may be non-typical. By inference from site examinations the majority of circles give the appearance of having expanded outwards from a centre, either rapidly with a radial blast or, by a display of spirality more or less manifest, and with varying degrees of strength down to comparative gentleness. In the absence of video-film analysis and additional eye-witness descriptions we must rely on deducing what we can from the frozen-in history of the vortex. This is done by inspecting the lying and the untouched straws, and by locating and analysing whenever possible *incomplete circles and rings which have imperfections of various kinds.*

Many questions can yet be posed.

Are there occasions when the flattening of the common circle commences with a *ring*, small or large, which subsequently expands or contracts until the whole area is flattened?

Two unmistakeable cases composed of an annular ring only, with others spotted from the air, have been fully surveyed. A photograph of part of one of these is reproduced in Figure 34. This was found at Kimpton in north-west

Fig.34: Part of the Kimpton ring, June 1987, a clockwise ellipse in a field of wheat. The breadth of the arc, some 30 metres in length, was between 0.3 and 0.4 metre.

Hampshire in June 1987. The clockwise, quasi-elliptical ring was extremely narrow. For much of its length it was less than 0.6 metre wide. The air movement which blew down the stems of the winter barley did its job with exemplary precision and delicacy. One may compare the achievement with the rotating sheath of a waterspout, even to the thinness of the wall. This is the kind of ring, broad or narrow in size, that may be expected to interlink satellite circles on occasions of good intra-satellite-ring development. But what are we to make of a very slight depression noted at the ring's centre where the barley was otherwise unharmed? The straws were parted at a narrow angle as if the point of a tapering cone had penetrated nearly to the ground for an instant. Might this have been the start of an expanding circle, had it continued? The field in which the ring was found had four or five small fully-flattened circles in it, one just fifty metres to the north.

Another ring was examined with considerable care at Westbury, Wiltshire, in August 1987 (Figure 35). This was clockwise, elliptical, and some ten metres south of the big anticlockwise circle shown at the end of this book (Figure 43). For us it was notable that the ring was incomplete. The agent that had marked it out so finely had barely reached or interacted with ground level before rising again in a series of undulations around the ring. This created gaps where the damaging agent had seemingly leapt across part of the arc leaving straws untouched (or at least it had applied so feeble a pressure that the straws had recovered their positions). This suggests that a species of rotating system

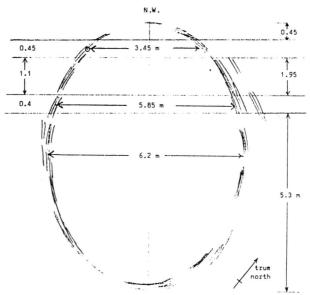

Fig.35: Survey details of the clockwise ring at Westbury, August 1987.

had hovered close to but above the field, and had barely dug into the crop at all, or that the ring resulted from the action of an inclined vortex tube. At Kimpton the damaging agent had exerted rather more pressure than this, even to the point of leaving a faint depression in the middle, but at Westbury we can say that proof of a central depression was certainly absent because it was specifically looked for.

Indications of hovering, or long-distance action via vortex-tube, when it is less than this soon reaches vanishing point. We can therefore never know in the total absence of field-trace marks (i.e. by negative information) how many 'plasmoids' might have hovered at non-touching distances. An absence of evidence is not evidence of absence. Bearing in mind the observations reported in Section 5.3 on the skimming effect, we can only say that *hovering is a deduced characteristic for some plasmoids, just as is 'descent and dissolution' and 'descent and re-ascent', and that such behaviour may be expected of plasmoids which although possibly invisible by day may be sufficiently well illuminated to be seen at night.* To obtain further documentation along these lines we shall pursue eye-witness accounts of the motion of what we may generalize as 'balls of light' with or without audible acoustic effects (next chapter).

5.8 TUFTS, MISSED CURVING SECTIONS, BEDS AND EDGES

We could go into much detail about the beds and perimeters of simple and complex circles but do not have the space in this introductory book. Only a few additional points will be made, and then in a general fashion, because some

Fig.36: Sketch of the single circle on Longwood Estate July 1987, showing two arcs of standing wheat (not drawn to scale). The metric measurements are taken from the spiral centre. Note the step on the southern side near the tractor lane. The photograph shows the 2.0-metre arc from its south-eastern end. The ranging rod is painted in 0.1 metre sections.

may have a bearing on the character of the agency at work.

Sometimes tufts, arcs or small irregular areas are left standing or partly standing after the departure of the damaging vortex. Only once prior to 1989 has a prominent tuft been spotted close to a centre; but in 1989 some 10 occurrences were noted (cf p.111).

The next plan from Hampshire (July 1987) introduces a mystery that is rather different (Figure 36). In two places it seems that the damaging agent during the course of its outward spiralling failed to strike down an arc within the body of the circle. It seemed not to be a question of fallen straws standing upright again but rather, it was the likelihood that the straws had never been hit over at all.

Circle beds are often multi-centred, bi-layered and highly complex at the edges and elsewhere. Bi-layering of a big anticlockwise circle at Headbourne Worthy, Hampshire, has been discussed in detail[3]. The plan, part of which is after Mr C. Andrews (Figure 7), provides varied evidence of subsidiary vortical and maybe pulsating motions. The author's conclusion is that this is a statement of expansion and retraction, probably connected with 'descent and re-ascent'.

Twin centering, which is commonly encountered, adds to the complexity and (with multi-layering and certain peculiar circumferential effects) would render impracticable any attempts by humorous hoaxers to deceive the author with imitations.

As for perimeters, they are not all as sharp as people think Many of the photographs in this book are of circles having what one might call a classical cut-off. This happens when a force vector having pursued a spiral course from the centre has degenerated into a circular one. The straws are then lying perpendicular to the radius. On the other hand many circumferences are indented in some way. The most commonly noted imperfection is a circumference with a peaked or spiked effect, as if injected by puffs during the last moments of the expanding mode of the primary vortex (cf sketch in Figure 7). Sometimes a step is noted on a perimeter, just one, as if created by a bunched 'parcel' of ions in its terminal mode. We have not the space to treat this here, but merely take the opportunity to point out that the uneven rotation of 'ion-parcels' like this could explain the kind of omitted arc mentioned in the preceding section (cf Figure 36).

The circles in the next figure (37) relate to a quintuplet formed on Beckhampton Down in August 1987. The nearest circles in this picture began with anticlockwise motion outwards from their centres, but as the radius increased a counterwise tendency set in which caused radial penetration of the standing crop in the manner indicated. When this is carried further, the straw pattern develops into an S-shape as the angles of the straws remote from the centre develop a clockwise trend.

A meaningful oddity which is often seen is an edge effect arising from the proximity of tractor-lanes to the circle circumference. The lanes are made by farm-tractors at sowing time, and are followed by the tractors to lessen

Fig.37: Part of the quintuplet circle system on Mr Stephen Horton's land on Beckhampton Down in September 1987. Diameter of the anticlockwise central circle was 13 metres while the satellite diameters ranged from 7.7 to nearly nine metres.

subsequent damage during crop-spraying operations. The edge of an expanding circle often distorts when a tractor lane is close because the peripheral stalks are less well supported when their neighbours are missing. Of course, a very considerable force is required to blow down stalks in an unblemished field because as the pressure on them rises they lie against all their neighbours which stand along the same line of action as the applied force.

At the other extreme one occasionally finds straws lying radially into the standing corn as a result of a radial blast of purely star-burst type. This leads us to tackle another puzzle, although its underlying nature is self-evidently different, and that is the unexpected problem of spurs.

5.9 SPURS

In a problem dominated by circular-symmetric patterning the linear effects which erupt as radially-directed spurs (Sections 1.9, 3.4) are dramatic exceptions.

Fine examples of short ones, a metre or less in length, were noted at Norton Bavant, West Wiltshire in July 1988 (Figure 13 shows a circumferential-radial junction). The longest known so far (from South Wiltshire) had a length of 14 metres, its remote end rounded both transversely and vertically (Figure 12).

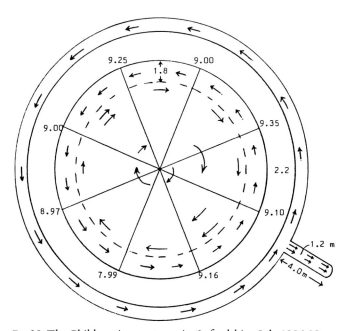

Fig.38: The Childrey rings and spur in Oxfordshire, July 1986. Note the unusual contra-rotation sections in the inner circle (as in Figure 11) and the radially-directed spur four metres long and 1.2 metres wide.

One of intermediate length was studied at Childrey, Oxfordshire, in 1986 after the completion of harvesting. A plan is given in Figure 38 which shows the spur extending radially from the outer ring. It is likely that a disturbance and small hole noted in the soil beyond the end of the spur were the work of a wild animal.

From what could be learnt about the most likely formation dates in the Oxfordshire and the two Wiltshire incidents it seems that the spurs could have been oriented with the geostrophic wind (the wind-of-the-day). It is as though something particulate (possibly as a 'parcel'), having circulated in the outer ring, had gathered at a point of the outer circle on the remote side from the wind direction, and had then been carried off in the direction of the wind at the termination of the incident. The straws of the Oxfordshire spur were pressed hard to the ground; those of the South Wiltshire spur seemed only lightly brushed. In the South Wiltshire case shown in Figure 12 the spur corresponded to the area of weakness proceeding from the presence of the parallel tractor-lanes. In fact, as commonly arises in farming, the crop-sowing direction was perpendicular to the field edge and parallel to the downslope direction. One may here speculate that, as the central force-field died out, the ion assembly induced in the outer ring was carried away by the wind-of-the-day, but due to the tractor-lane weakness it felled only the straws in the impaired region. At the time of writing this seems to be one of the hardest mysteries to explain, but some comment was necessary because I have so often been asked to attempt an explanation. Unfortunately the evidence available on this aspect of the subject is severely limited, and the present thoughts are liable to undergo considerable revision when more exactly-dated circles can be examined.

5.10 VORTEX BREAKDOWN

The discovery in August 1989 of numerous circles with standing stalks at their spiral centres (pp.70, 116) provide good visible support *for vortex breakdown as a major mechanism for circle production* (cf. p.38, ref.21; see also H. J. Lugt, *Bull. Amer. Met. Soc.* Vol.20, 1526-1537, Dec. 1989, for a general introduction to vortex breakdown in atmospheric columnar vortices). Swirling ring vortices have recently been treated theoretically by H. K. Moffat (*Fluid Dynamics Research,* Vol.1, 3, 22-30, 1988) and the principle applied to the circles effect in papers prepared for publication in 1990/91 by Drs. Tokio Kikuchi, John T. Snow and the author. The front of the expanding ring can induce a separation which produces secondary counterflowing currents leading to flattened rings on occasion (cf. the smoke-ring experiments of H. Yamada, T. Kohsaka, H. Yamabe and T. Matsui: Flowfield produced by a vortex ring near a plane wall. *J. Phys. Soc. Japan,* Vol.51, 1663-1670, 1982). Quintuplet vortices might similarly be related to surface-boundary effects. If so, the circulating air within rings and satellites could transport charged particles in the airflow and create the electrically-active rings and circles.

Chapter Six

VORTICES AND BALLS OF LIGHT

And the light shineth in darkness;
and the darkness comprehended it not.

St. John, i. 5.

6.1 VORTICES AND SPINNING BALLS

Thus far we have explored the circles for traces of their origins, and have found they are caused by the arrival of a spinning wind, a mass of air which, like dust-devil whirlwinds and tornadoes, is probably always partially ionized.

The circular symmetry behoves an axial symmetric system or vortex as the basic configuration of the damaging agent. It is likely that the vortex originates in a columnar tube or pipe well above ground level. Therefore, it would commence with cylindrical symmetry, which, as the ion concentration increases, would tend to metamorphose into a sphere given the presence of a surface force or tension between ionized and non-ionized states. For high spin-rates a transition to a flattened spheroid or discoid may be expected.

Very considerable proof has been amassed from ground-trace studies which shows that the circle-making vortex or spinning plasma-ball comes into contact with the ground sometimes gently, sometimes with great force. Indications for hovering are provided by a weak brushing of the crop-surface, as noted on occasions (Sections 5.3, 5.7), and incomplete formations on others. Eye-witness sightings of different swirled or spiral-circles in the course of formation suggest the rolling of a vortex about a pivoting tip (Section 2.2, 3.5).

Other known properties of the circles-effect vortex include luminous and acoustic effects, and the production of radio-frequency emissions, all symptomatic of electromagnetism and intimating that the vortices serve as model electromagnetic generators.

At night therefore under optimal atmospheric conditions lights may be expected. They may be seen either diving hard at the ground or descending gently and then perhaps receding, or just vanishing into nothing. The plasma-vortex balls or plasmoids may be thought of as a ball-lightning analogue although bigger in size and much longer lived. As we shall see, there is no shortage of good observations of such phenomena in collections and in the published literature, but despite a high credibility rating for a substantial number, they have not previously been collated into a coherent package and presented for scientific perusal. We therefore provide a select few in this book while reserving a greater number for publication on another occasion.

6.2 BALLS OF LIGHT

We start by scrutinizing our own databanks. When the Tornado and Storm Research Organisation (T.O.R.R.O.) began in 1974, one of its aims was to assemble for study everything that could be collected on the subject of tornadoes, waterspouts, lesser whirlwinds and other vortices, deluges of rain, damaging windstorms, remarkable showers, hailstorms, thunderstorms *and ball lightning*. All literary sources were inspected, the chief work being carried out by Michael Rowe and the author, and a press-cutting service subscribed to. Then about ten years ago Michael initiated a bold undertaking: he would appeal through the press for unknown reports from the British public, and he began by writing to some 2000 newspapers, a few each week. In 1988 having reached the newspaper which terminates the alphabet, he has started again, writing to the multitude of new papers founded since the work began. The result has been the compilation of a great private collection which is being analysed for the public good, and regarding which reports have appeared regularly in *The Journal of Meteorology* since 1975.

Let us consider the ball lightning files. The instability of ball lightning being well-known, we initially followed the traditional approach of attaching great weight to lightning balls having short lifetimes while assigning lower weight to those with long lifetimes. Now we see that the reverse may be nearer the truth. So many of the short-lived events (those with lifetimes of a few seconds or less) can be explained away for various good reasons[48]) that it diminishes the stock of possibly reliable short-lived incidents. But the longer-lived ones, till now thought 'theoretically' impossible by most ball-lightning researchers, can at last be accounted for by a previously-unrecognized phenomenon: the vortex-stabilized, 'pipe-fed' plasma ball responsible for the circles effect. For convenience, we distinguish these balls from the traditional ones by calling them 'balls of light'.

More recently, the author undertook his own appeal specifically aimed at recovering incidents involving such balls of light from the public. In what follows we choose a selection of accounts from the primary T.O.R.R.O. collection (M. Rowe's appeal), the author's special appeal (which is continuing – additional reports always welcome), Mark Stenhoff's collection[48] (a few were published in his *Ball Lightning Newsletter,* since discontinued), and from the general literature. Many incidents from the latter, it will be seen, having been classed 'unassignable' by their first investigators seem to have passed into the broad spectrum of that catch-all category known as 'unidentified flying objects'. Yet the ball-of-light phenomena that we are studying are not solid 'objects'; nor do they 'fly'. They are aerial or atmospheric spinning phenomena, hitherto unidentified but now endowed with scientific sanctuary via the known laws of physics.

6.3 HOVERING BALL IN NOTTINGHAMSHIRE

The first account is on the whole quite unremarkable. We provide it because it is *so typical* of many. The letter from Mrs Thelma Lavin of Langold, Worksop, to Michael Rowe was dated 16 October 1984.

'Re your letter in the *Worksop Guardian* a couple of weeks ago. Although I am not sure whether my sighting was a ball lightning or not. I will tell you what I saw, then you will probably be able to enlighten me, as I have never found out what I saw might have been. I am going back to June 10th 1982 at around 2 a.m. I saw what looked like a great ball of light hanging about Telegraph Pole height across over the field which looks over the back of my house. It had what I can only explain what looked like very long sparks falling away from it on to the ground. It must have been there for between 5 to 10 minutes before it gradually disappeared. One was almost mesmerized by it. The weather was a cool dry day. My information is quite correct as I have it in my diary!

This appears to be an authentic unexaggerated observation, supported by helpful diary notes.

6.4 HOVERING ORANGE-RED LIGHT IN BATH, NOVEMBER 1977

This account has similarities with the last. The author Mrs Olive Bessant sent the author a water-colour painting, prepared the day after the incident, showing three stages of the sighting with times and other details. It is reproduced in Figure 39 which unfortunately loses in monochrome the usefulness of the colour rendering. The central region was red and shaped like a burning log, with a yellowish aura all about it 'like a bright lit-up candle'. Note that the phenomenon dissipates by dissolving into thin air 'as though it was in a cylinder'.

'On reading your article in last Thursday's *Evening Chronicle* I knew it was my opportunity to write to you. I'm afraid it was a long time ago in 1977. I was in a bed-sit at no 20 Bloomfield Road, Bath, and I had a lovely view from my window with a big expanse of sky. Sometimes I used to watch the planes go by with my binoculars, as straight across in the distance was the Bristol Channel with Bristol on the far right. It was on the Sunday night at about midnight on 6-11-77 when I pulled back the curtains before I went to bed. In the distance

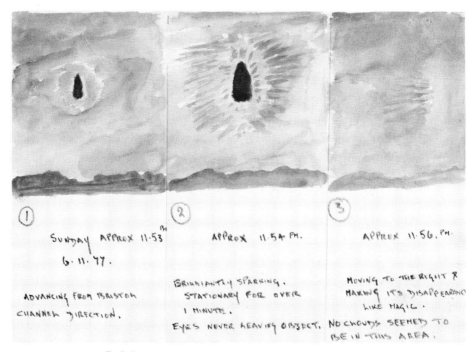

Fig.39: Memorandum notes and painting by Mrs Olive Bessant of Bath who watched while a light, described as red like a burning log and surrounded by a yellow glow, approached and hovered close to her apartment on the south-western outskirts of the city. As the self-luminous light weakened, "it gradually made its disappearance as though it was in a cylinder". The date was 6 November 1977.

from the direction of the channel I saw what looked like a bright lit-up candle slowly approaching in a straight line coming my way. It came over the allotments and stopped over 2 elm trees at the bottom of the garden. I could see then that it was like a burning log showering sparks everywhere for about a minute. Then turning slowly to the right, it gradually made its disappearance as though it was in a cylinder. It was a bit scary and I was afraid to blink although I was fascinated'.

The remark 'as though it was in a cylinder' classes the episode as *a tubular vortex occurrence,* linked to the illuminated tubes discussed previously (Section 4.7).

6.5 ELECTROMAGNETIC EFFECTS FROM LUMINOUS BALL NEAR WESTBURY WHITE HORSE

The next is a recent incident which provides sound, luminosity, and radio-frequency radiation in an area of Wessex frequently subject to the circles effect. It is the first of the 'car-stop' incidents to be described. In the last two summers circles have been found to the west close by in an adjacent field of wheat, while twenty-five circles have appeared in the fields just below the escarpment to the north.

I interviewed the witness on 13 January 1989. His frightening experience happened a year before, on the night of 22-23 January 1988. A C.B. enthusiast he often spent the night on the high ground adjoining the White Horse for the purpose of long-distance transmissions. The weather was clear and frosty. Around 1 a.m. while operating the radio the equipment suddenly went dead as if a fuse had blown. Having no spare fuse, his reaction was to start the car in order to return home – but the ignition was unaccountably dead. Some fifteen seconds having passed since the interruption began, he became aware of an external humming noise which he likened to the hum one can hear near electric power lines. He then became aware of a glow developing about him which, like the hum, came from *above* his vehicle. The light rapidly intensified and illuminated brilliantly an area some ten metres or more in diameter. Then after a total of ten seconds since the light was noticed, it 'went out' which it did by diffusing away, as if 'evaporating'. The main volume of the light was white but towards the edges it was a 'dull orange'. Terrified he tried the ignition again, and it worked!, upon which he left at once for home.

The *Daily Weather Summary* charts of the Meteorological Office, together with my weather diary notes showed that after rain had stopped at 09 on 22nd January sunny periods developed in a north-westerly airstream. A clear evening followed as a ridge of high pressure crossed the region. The wind was light at midnight, westerly or near calm, which suggested well-stratified stable moist air. But the next weather front was approaching and the wind started backing and began to pick up again. We surmise that in the westerly airflow the plasma vortex developed overhead possibly in a trailing-vortex system where turbulence at a point along a line of separation upset a smoother stable flow. This could have provoked vortex 'breakdown' and led to the radio-frequency plasma whose total recorded lifetime in the neighbourhood of the vehicle was 25 seconds. Note that the undoubted plasma never reached the ground (so no circle would have been made) but its other observed properties of light, sound and radio-frequency energy were indisputably accompanied by a 'hovering' and a 'dissolution into thin air' as related in the two preceding letters.

Slow-moving or hovering lights of obscure origin which definitely have no military connection are not uncommon on or close to the Westbury-Bratton-Tinhead Hills. We know of several, the latest of which happened on the top ridge of Tinhead Hill, at 21 hours in late November or early December 1988.

6.6 CAR STOP EVENT BY COLLOWAY CLUMP

I am often asked about the circles 'that never were', those non-events which one would expect now and then because the circle-making agent missed the field of crops. These must occur in their thousands for every one that hits a sufficiently mature crop as to leave an indelible impression. Some of the vortices that miss fields of crops hit houses (as reviewed in Section 2.5), some hit people (Section 2.3), and some hit roads or motor vehicles.

This next incident happened on the Westbury road a little north of Warminster at the Colloway Clump bend before the last turning back to Upton Scudamore for a driver going south. The date was 7 September 1965 and the time between 19 and 1930 GMT. Being twilight and not yet dark, any luminosity was too weak to be noticed[49].

It was while travelling in top gear at 45 m.p.h. that the engine of Major Hill's car cut out. As it came to a halt the car shuddered 'under the down-beating pressure of aerial vibrations. For a time the Major felt a rolling motion beneath him as the whole bodywork swayed . . . his headlights flickered, lacking power. The convulsions of the car subsided enough for him to jump out . . . However, he was immediately conscious of air vibrations of a violent character which surrounded and beat down on him, and heard a sinister whining and crackling . . . (He said) "It was on a par with the sounds of high-powered refrigeration units or deep-freeze equipment, but far away above that level, magnified many times. After less than three minutes everything was back to normal. I pressed the starter button, and the car purred away perfectly, just as if it had never been halted at all". He further affirmed that the decisive peculiarity of his experience was that there was "a definite impression of something pressing down on me with force. It was distinctly uncanny".

Using the *Daily Weather Summary* I found that the regional geostrophic flow that evening was south-westerly. After the light winds of a ridge of high pressure, the wind had picked up as a south-westerly. A sharp hill was close by on the east and south-east (Colloway and Arn Hill), so the vortex could have formed immediately to the windward of these slopes if the local wind was south-west (or in the lee if the local wind was south-east). In another incident which happened before dawn in almost the same spot one month earlier the vortex plasma struck in a clear lee situation, the wind being east-south-east to east. This is what is described next.

6.7 TRUCK HIT SPINNING 'BALL OF LIGHT'

The time was 0336 GMT on 10 August 1965 as the southbound truck went round the bend by Colloway Clump and met a ball of crimson light which got struck while braking[50].

'. . . the orb virtually fastened on to his windscreen without shattering the glass . . . The truck ended up by the wire fencing on the offside, just short of the triangle of grass beside the signpost to the village of Upton Scudamore . . . Only then did the crimson body of the thing spin away. The bright circle detached itself and soared aloft. The driver said: "It was so huge; much larger than my truck. I would say it measured a good thirty to forty feet across at the base (say 9-12 metres). When it was fixed to the windscreen it . . . kicked up

Fig.40: Lower picture: The bend by Colloway Clump with two circles near it, photographed in July 1988. A third circle 200 metres away in the distance is shown again in the upper photograph (aerial shots from a Cessna piloted by Michael Rutty).

enormous vibrations, yet the glass did not break". The driver also reported a whistling sound as the orb spun away. The same day but one hour earlier at a place a couple kilometres further south came a report of a similar phenomenon with a droning sound that dissolved *in situ* without reaching the ground.

Between them, all the characteristics now known or inferred for *spinning plasma vortices* are present in these vehicular incidents by Colloway Clump: spin, air-motion, downward pressure, noise, radio-frequency effects, self-luminosity, and size. Furthermore, they took place in a region which since 1983 we have known is prone to vortex-circle formation in crops. The aerial photographs taken in July 1988 show three circles in the wheatfield adjoining the A350 highway (Figure 40). Two circles are next to the very bend in the road mentioned in both accounts and another is close to the triangle of grass referred to in the second. On the basis of these incidents I think we have gained a very fair idea of what it would be like to be hit by the luminous plasma of a descending circles-effect vortex, not forgetting also the experiences described in Section 2.3 to which another will be added in 6.11 below.

Many circles are known for this part of West Wiltshire. In an adjoining field a quintuplet appeared in 1987, and the following year on the other side of a lane now cut by the new by-pass, a quintuplet formed in 1988. Large single circles were found close by in 1983 and 1986. In fact, our archive includes several sightings of balls of light at low level or ground level for this neighbourhood, further details of which will be recounted elsewhere.

6.8 BALL OF LIGHT SHATTERS CAR WINDSCREEN

Out of the many dozens of records upon which we can draw we choose the next because it is a recent case which takes us to the margins where uncertainty presides regarding whether we are dealing with ball lightning, as commonly understood, or not. It was reported in Mark Stenhoff's *Ball Lightning Newsletter,* no 2, 1985. The event's explosive decay has features in common with ball lightning but the total absence of thundery conditions might count against its being ball lightning.

'Mr D. K. Hughes, a farmer, was driving his van along the A40 road near the Haverfordwest Golf Club, Pembrokeshire, Wales. "It was raining heavily when in front of me I saw a ball of fire the size of the front wheel of a tractor. The van lit up, then there was a big bang and the windscreen shattered". The event occurred on 4 or 5 April 1985 at about 1220. There was no storm connected, and no thunder or lightning. The ball was first seen in mid-air some way above the road. It was spherical and red, and bright enough to be clearly visible in daylight. The ball was uniformly illuminated across its surface, and its appearance did not change much during the event. The van windscreen was completely shattered by the explosion . . . The event was brought to my attention by Mr Ian Jones, a meteorologist operating a station some 22km away. Mr Jones reports that there were no days with thundery conditions around 4/5 April. He kindly provided a barogram showing that the pressure on 4 April fell from 1008mb at midnight to 994mb at 1500, remaining fairly steady throughout April 5.

This was a car-stop phenomenon of a different character if it is the truth that the windscreen broke because of a decisive disintegration of the ball, rather than a flying stone, say (the fact that 'the van lit up' implies a close approach of the 'ball of light'). In that event, the action indicated irrevocable instability of the constituent material, perhaps triggered by a cooling effect brought on by the cold rain.

6.9 FAILURE OF AUTOMOBILE IGNITION SYSTEMS

Car stop events with light-ball associations close by are relatively numerous world-wide. A compilation by G. Falla found 420 reported cases in a 30-year period to 1977[51]. One may wonder how it is that the ignition systems fail, as they undoubtedly do.

In most reported events car-ignition failure and/or loss of lights is a temporary condition. When the incident ends, the electrics work again. Less commonly, the breakdown is irreversible. We provide a double car-stop story as an example[52].

In the autumn of 1968 or 1969 Mr John Turner, who is now a B.B.C. television and radio features presenter in Bristol, was in a car with three passengers (one being Ralph MacTal of the London Troubadors) driving east along the A4 highway. About 2 a.m. they were nearing the Beckhampton cross-roads in mid-Wiltshire when a red sports car overtook them. Seconds later the passengers spotted a bright light nearby as their car spluttered to a halt. The motor would not restart, so the Royal Automobile Club was informed, with the result that the car was towed to the garage of a nearby town. Soon afterwards the red sports car was pulled in as well! It had broken down just a little further on than John Turner's car. Amazing to relate, the wiring looms of both automobiles had shorted and burnt out.

Can this ever have been a coincidence? A loom burn-out is uncommon at any time in the world of automobiles, but here we have simultaneous burn-outs to independent cars at the same place. What kind of electric and magnetic field effects can influence motor-car performance? It must be said that the area where the two cars failed is at the heart of the Yatesbury/Avebury/Silbury region where so many circles-effect vortices reappear each year.

Firstly, we may accept the experimental tests carried out at a major national laboratory in the U.S.A. which showed that magnetic fields do not affect the components of automobile ignition systems except at improbably-high intensities[44]. For example, the spark of an aluminium-contained coil started missing at around 4000 gauss and failed at 17 000, whereas the lights were unaffected up to the imposed field limit of 20 000 gauss. A car having its ignition coil protected in a steel casing would continue to operate to 20 000 gauss. In practice, the metal shielding provided by the car's bodywork would protect the system to much higher magnetic fields.

Experiments using electric fields are not known to have been attempted. Roy Craig[44] commented that any hypothesis that ionized air may affect internal combustion was not likely because 'no concomitant physiological or physical effects that such ionization would cause are reported'.

This statement is certainly erroneous. Many accounts of physiological effects exist for people caught outdoors rather than within the partially protected environment of sealed automobiles. so it is opportune to review some of the known material.

6.10 PHYSIOLOGICAL EXPERIENCES NEAR SPINNING VORTICES

We begin with the common dust-devil. Although well-studied with regard to their formation and physical characteristics, the electrostatic and ionization properties have been investigated but little. In Section 4.2 we summarized what is known of the electric fields they create. Fast spin rates create ion and electron assemblies with a high space-charge density and high electric fields (approaching – 1580 volts/m at a distance of 245 metres in the case of one 15-metre diameter devil)[30]. Due to leakages of charge into the counterflowing part of the circulation, some ionized particles must get transported away from the main gyrating current. These can explain physiological effects noted for animals for instance.

Consider the summer whirlwind at Horton, near Devizes on 28 June 1857. A 12-acre field of clover was lying in cock when a 'whirl-puff' arrived and started lifting the cocks into the air. Mr William Brown, the farmer, being on horseback rode in the direction that the whirlwind was taking in order to ascertain its cause. He said that he encountered not the least breath of air, but as he got nearer 'nothing would induce his horse to face it – not on account of any rush of wind (for of that there was little or none), but from a remarkable sensation, which made the animal stagger, and almost lifted Mr Brown from his seat'[53]. This recalls the Westbury incident of October 1986, recounted in Section 2.3, when one of two ladies, caught in a circles-effect vortex, made the diary entry that their dog Bing 'went wild'. They said that the behaviour of the animal became quite abnormal for a time and was wholly uncharacteristic of the dog. Animals seem to encounter physiological effects initiated by the electric field, besides perhaps hearing acoustic sounds inaudible to humans.

Physiological effects on humans are similarly known, and several will be referred to in our next book. Here, we confine ourselves to a single example which embraces all the known elements of a circles-effect vortex and includes physiological effects besides.

6.11 GROUNDED BY A CIRCLES-EFFECT VORTEX

Late on 28 March 1965, at 23 hours, Mr Eric Payne (19) was walking into the village of Bishopstrow, Wiltshire, from the south.

"I had reached a point near Drayton's School, a little short of the bend in the road, when I heard a whistling noise that developed into a loud buzzing. It was not coming from the telegraph wires by the roadside, though it was similar to that kind of humming. I am not too sure from which direction it came. Fog was so thickly banked-up by then that it blotted out most of the sky. It was pitch dark anyway. Then the object made itself felt. It flattened treetops on either side of me, making a tremendous racket overhead . . . I looked up to see if it was a low-flying plane. I felt great pressure on my head and neck. Something stung my hands and cheeks. I lifted my fists and tried to fight it off". A knife-edged wind tore through his hair and burned at his eyes, it was so fierce and keen. "Before it came for me I could spot nothing in the sky except a shadow. It was lighter in colour and shaped like an oval dish. The light was very poor. It could easily have been a bank of mist rising, as no aircraft lights or anything like that were visible. But it set up a jarring clatter, jumble and clanging that no plane could ever make! It was the shrill whining and buzzing which nearly drove me mad. My head was pushed from side to side and I might as well have left my arms and legs at home for all the use they were. I simply could not stop this tremendous downward pressure. I crawled round in the road for a bit and then sank to my knees on the grass verge, which was soaking wet. But that did not worry me. All I wanted was to get rid of the choking hold the thing had on me". He said that the back of his neck was raw with cold, yet when it had all started he could feel heat and a prickling feeling, as though sharp needles were digging into his flesh. Eventually, the wind stopped and Mr Payne made on homewards[54].

Bishopstrow is close to Sutton Veny and Tytherington whose fields we know to be subject to circles-effect vortices. We note that the main physiological sensations are: prickling, body weakness (notably in the legs), and choking. The mention of heat may be a 'relative' one, due to warmer air being brought down by the vortex, or it may be the warmth generated by recombination processes. The statement of descending air currents is once again overwhelming, and it accords with all the evidence known for the crop-traces circles-effect.

6.12 DAYTIME SIGHTINGS OF SHINY ELLIPSOIDS AND LIKE PHENOMENA

On 6 January 1989 I received a phone call from Mr Dennis Hawkes who on 20 August 1965 had visited Corsley Heath, a village not far from Cley Hill on the Frome-Warminster road. The day had been warm with ten hours of sunshine, and the wind west to south-westerly (regional weather information from *Daily Weather Report*). At 5 p.m. looking with his brother towards Chapmanslade two kilometres away he spotted a hovering cigar-shaped ellipsoid which remained in sight for half-a-minute. Its length-to-width ratio was 4 or 5 to 1. The angular size was similar to that of the church (20 metres long, say). Although the colour was a *solid* white or perhaps whitish-yellow, the observed form faded *by becoming grainy* while yet retaining a definite outline until it completely vanished into thin air. Such behaviour would comply with the expected properties of a vortex of vaporous air or ionized air.

This leads to the question of so-called shiny or metallic objects seen by daylight in low-level hovering positions. There are innumerable reports of this kind, some from irreproachable witnesses. Is a rational explanation available to link any of them with the properties of the atmosphere and/or with circles-effect vortices?

Let us recall the effect in the circles-traces of the sharp perimeters and the narrow rings. We have proposed that the rings may arise from windflow action activated by an induced electromagnetic current (Section 5.6); and we suggest further that their sharpness may be linked to an interfacial or surface-tension effect separating the plasmoid and non-plasmoid states.

The idea of a boundary effect in the form of a contracting force came from the Swedish physicist Carl Benedicks[55]. He gives an acceptable argument that a surface-tension causing a discontinuity must be expected at the limiting surface between a hot and a cooler gas, and considers the case in which the latter is moist air and the former is charged air with thermally-dissociated hydrogen and oxygen. Benedicks remarks that the surface discontinuity is analogous to the one surrounding an air-bubble in water. The consequence is an evenly-reflecting surface with the illusion of metallic lustre. Although there is no evidence that the plasma postulated for the circles-effect vortex is hot (it may sometimes, perhaps, be warm), the concept of a discontinuity between plasma and non-plasma states is to be respected, besides which there may be high-humidity occasions when it is vapour-filled as well. This may suffice to account for world-wide reported observations of such reflective, vaporous entities.

The equilibrium state is a sphere, but, if the surrounding air is flowing, an elongated shape results – ellipsoidal or cigar-shaped. And when the mass is spinning, as always in a vortex, the shape is flattened to a lesser or greater degree into a flattened-ellipsoidal or discoidal form. Thus we approach, more and more closely, the classic vision of a metallic object in the daytime sky which, however, by consisting of nothing more than the constituents of the atmosphere, can dissolve and rematerialize with incorporeal ease.

Although a mass of air suspended within a surrounding mass of air is difficult to perceive, there now seem to be two circumstances where its discernment is facilitated. The familiar one is when the former is so heavily laden with water vapour that cloud droplets condense out (this gives an exterior which appears smooth and regular when spinning). The new one arises when it is a question of a spinning plasma. This sharpness between states of matter, aided by a postulated interfacial tension, can explain the neatness of the narrow rings introduced in Sections 1.7, 5.4 and 5.5, and discussed in 5.5.

Thus depending on charge density, recombination rates, humidity factors, dust content, etc, we have constructed a picture of what plasma vortex-balls may look like both by night and by day. Due to a lack of understanding about the reality of such a relatively long-lived plasma ball, earlier sightings have been mostly set aside as 'inexplicable', even if reliably reported by trained, articulate scientists (cf the ball-of-light report by a nuclear physicist in Section 7.7), because of a lack of established theory. But a coherent picture is emerging which embraces a broad range of properties and have a persuasive strength in their totality. Consolidation and summary of all aspects introduced in this book is what we attend to in the next, our final chapter.

Chapter Seven

SYNTHESIS

Nature and Nature's laws lay hid in night:
God said, "Let Newton be!" and all was light.
Alexander Pope, Epistles of Horace.

7.1 THE CIRCLES-EFFECT VORTEX

Our objective has been to examine the remarkable patterns and ground traces which appear in the fields of Britain every summer, and other countries besides, for the information they offer about the atmospheric processes producing the circles. Our assessment of the evidence is that they are the result of a previously-unrecognized species of atmospheric plasma vortex. The vortex has affinities with ball lightning plasma, but differs from it in various ways, notably by its larger size and capacity for longer-life. Although we infer that the time taken to mark out the circular ground traces is short, the postulated vortices seem able to persist for extended intervals of time on account of mechanical forcing and a charging process engineered by organized turbulent motions in the air. Such vortices and the consequent 'circles effect' are capable of creation at any time of year if atmospheric circumstances permit. It is only because the crops are in their most vulnerable condition in the late spring and summer that the patterns which so appeal to the aesthetic senses of onlookers arise frequently in those seasons. At other times and in other places there are alternative effects which may be noted by the diligent observer (hollows cleared in the ground, water blasted from wet-land areas, humming noises, optical and radio-frequency effects, etc). These are all manifestations of the same vortex which on descending to ground level in the presence of a crop is Creatrix of the circles effect, like Ceres the Roman corn goddess.

We have covered a broad expanse of material in our quest for a solution, and have tried to weld it into a unified scheme. Additionally, the application of logic to what is known helps us generate ideas for the future (Section 7.8). This little book is to be regarded as no more than an introduction to the subject – a pause for consolidation while toiling at the frontiers of science in an area of research charged with mysteries and thrilling discoveries. Much more information will appear eventually in further works on the circles effect.

7.2 REMARKS ON ALTERNATIVE PROPOSALS REGARDING THE CIRCLES EFFECT

No other seriously-presented proposals as to the origin of the circles effect have appeared to date, but various loosely-phrased suggestions and wild guesses have been put forward. One set of these may be grouped together in a 'folk-lore' class of their own. They originate from countryfolk who speak of rutting deer, mating hedgehogs, and nurseries for vixens.

These ideas arise from putting the effect before the cause. Although erroneous, they have the merit of reminding us that the circles effect has its place in country lore, which helps to demonstrate a pre-modern age for the circles effect. If a farmer chances to find a freshly-laid circle with a herd of hedgehogs inside it, or notes the flight of deer upon his approach, he may mistake the animals for maker instead of finder. A Lancashire correspondent wrote to tell me that the circles there are known as snigs nests. A snig is a country name for eel, and is probably also applied to the snake. Nests made by vixens are mentioned at times. Another correspondent told me how when he was a prisoner-of-war in Austria near Graz in the 1940's such circles were found in the summer being used by deer as labour wards and nurseries. The satellite circles were joined to the main circle by narrow pathways trodden down by the animals.

Crop deficiencies of some kind receive attention now and then. For the B.B.C. film shown in October 1988 a soil expert was summoned to take samples. Patterned attacks by fungus are glibly proposed, or over-fertilization by crop sprayers, but the damage wreaked this way is wholly unrelated to the problem we are investigating. Farmers have told us, though, how astute rooks and crows can be at pulling down the stalks of immature corn in order to remove the soft unripe grain. These agents may damage corn in their own ways, but they have no relationship to the problem under study. We admit the possibility that crows may periodically swoop into circles already formed by the circles-effect vortex and take advantage of the open circumference by attacking the exposed edges. Some farmers may consequently have seen assaults on existing circles being made by birds in this way, which could therefore account for a few reported cases of circles apparently expanding their diameters during days subsequent to their first appearance.

Archaeologists are aware that crops grow more poorly over buried walls, more luxuriantly over ancient ditches. Thus cropmarks can be seen, especially in dry weather, via effects on growth rate and crop discoloration. This is, however, quite a different matter from the sudden flattening of crops into spirals and circles in the space of a few seconds which is the 'circles effect'.

A remark is needed about hovering helicopters. Their downdraughts spread out and ripple across an extensive area, never producing a sharply delimited circle as in the circles effect. Despite that, it is conceivable that helicopters could produce circles by another mechanism, because, like aeroplanes they can throw out short-lived trailing vortices from the tips of the main rotor. One Wiltshire farmer claims to have seen this happen some years ago. He may be right; but an investigator who arrives too late to check this out with a site visit would need to inquire into the circle size, details of the circle's bed, and the state of the atmosphere if known (including speed and direction of the wind), because the farmer could unwittingly be inverting the blame like the accusers of deer and hedgehogs. At all events, trailing-vortices issuing from helicopters would have small diameters (of the order of rotor-blade length at maximum). Bigger vortices are expected from bigger aircraft of course, but the aircraft trailing-vortex circles studied by the author prove that they could never be confused with natural vortex spiral-circles[56].

Hoaxed circles, or ones laid out for 'experimental' purposes, are known to have been made but rarely. From a distance one could be fooled but close inspection reveals the lack of complexity always present in the real thing (e.g. good spiral pattern, complex edge and bed effects). Chains, planks, human feet and rolling bodies have been employed in such attempts.

Some observers have at various times introduced ley lines into the plot[57]. These, we are told, are ancient world-wide 'energy paths'. As more and more circles were found each year it was necessary to broaden lines into 'corridors miles wide'. Of course, a few accidental or contrived correspondences always turn up eventually, but that is a consequence of the mathematics of statistics[58].

Other attempts at locating patterning have led Messrs C. Andrews and P. Delgado to see the circles as the work of some sort of 'intelligence'. Attention was directed at edge or centre alignments of circles with tractor-lanes, and claims made that the circles are intelligently locating themselves[59]. Poltergeist and paranormal phenomena take part in the claims.

Mr Delgado has hinted that there could be some link with sub-surface piezo-electric effects developing from stress build-up in fault zones beneath the earth's surface; the idea is that stress release sends piezo-electric waves spiralling upwards and out of the earth[60]. In 1987 Mr Delgado wrote "that UFOs could be manipulating *Earth Forces* to create these circles with such clean precision. This same precision may be responsible for the animal mutilations"[61]. It is only fair in a book on the circles effect to quote his recent opinions in detail[62]. Thus, "The configurations of these circles seem to be strongly symbolistic. The increasing complexities may be in the form of a challenge to us to de-code. They could symbolise all manner of subjects from evolution in cell structures to planets and asteroids revolving around the Earth. The contra-rotated swirls are a mystery in themselves. Maybe these circles are created by alien beings using force-field unknown to us. They may be manipulating existing Earth energy, the mysterious energies we know exist. . . If intelligent beings or an intelligence of some form is responsible for these circles, then the progressive complexity we have experienced in the past should provide some even more exciting investigations in 1987". In summer 1988 Mr Delgado was saying of the circles: "They are created by an unknown force, possibly manipulated by an unknown intelligence. Any natural force could not create such intriguing patterns".

Mr Andrews wrote in November 1987[63]: "During recent years it has been my pleasure to eliminate a number of alleged or possible causes for this phenomenon. These include: hoaxers; animals; weather and meteorological conditions; and chemicals. We are then left with some highly interesting and indeed bizarre possibilities. One thing remains certain. There are ever increasing indications that the source of this phenomenon is paranormal". At the same time evidence for a U.F.O. connection was advanced with regard to certain Hampshire episodes[63]. "The extensive data now gathered . . . indicates some form of intelligence is involved, probably working in tandem with the magnetic field around our planet and could be an aerial entity of some kind"[64]. It is hoped and expected that these authors will clarify their interpretations in a book *Circular Evidence* to be published in summer 1989. They will also need to substantiate their·claim that "the circles are always created at night" (cf our Sections 2.2 and 5.5, where daytime eye-witness reports are provided). Whatever happens, these authors have unequivocally and repeatedly stated their position regarding their rejection of a natural atmospheric solution, claiming in particular that the circles effect has nothing to do with weather and meteorological conditions, and that an intelligent hand of some sort is involved instead. What this might really mean has not been clarified, but it could involve for instance apparent alignments of axi-symmetric circle systems with tractor lanes or with the earth's magnetic field.

7.3 A TEST FOR ALIGNMENTS

So let us take a look at possible geomagnetic orientations and some tractor-lane alignments within the compass of quintuplet-arm orientations, chosen because each quintuplet has four satellites and four arms. From our discussions in previous chapters we anticipate that the local electrostatic field will be gravely modified at the time of circle-making activity. It might then be possible that the four antinodal plasma positions could reflect this situation following our anterior suggestion that their creation develops electromagnetically. Hence, two opposed satellites could be so aligned, or adjacent pairs might be aligned thus instead. Now look at the two quintuplet sets which stood opposite Silbury Hill in 1988 (Figure 41). These have obvious alignments, it is true, but they lie with tractor lanes, not with the earth's field. For the tractor lanes are oriented at 022 degrees east of magnetic north which only serves to demonstrate an absence of any magnetic correlation on these occasions.

But is there instead some 'intelligence' factor which is able to render the tractor lanes significant? Before answering this, one needs to assemble a large mass of data in order to treat it with due statistical reserve. We have tried it,

Fig.41: Complex of thirteen circles in a single field, formed in three episodes, July 1988. Look for two quintuplet sets in dice formation and three singlets. Compare this photograph with the one taken two weeks earlier (Figure 26) which shows only the first of the quintuplets.

but can only make the statement that there are insufficient data to make a valid statistical judgement. The difficulties are compounded because tractor lanes often follow field boundaries; field boundaries often follow hill ridges and slopes, or are perpendicular to them; and the possibility exists that some axes of quintuplet sets develop perpendicular/parallel to hill slopes (as could well have happened at Bratton, where the scarp and the road run from west-south-west to north-north-east). The effect can be seen in Figure 2 in which the tractor and combine lanes are oriented at 22 degrees west of true north (i.e. north-north-west) as against 18 degrees for the quintuplet arms. Figure 42 is broadly similar although the mismatch between lanes and arms is some eight degrees, the arms being further to the west than the tractor-lane direction which is around 15 degrees west of north.

It has been noted that a few single circles have appeared in the corners of fields, sometimes symmetrically placed with regard to nearby hedges. A symmetrical disposition could result from effects decided simply by local windflow conditions and/or a modified electrostatic field.

The results of comparing orientations of a major axis relative to the earth's field (which is six degrees west of true north) for 26 quintuplets may be grouped as follows:

Within +/- 6 degrees (approximately) of magnetic north, five events; within +/- 6 degrees of an angle which is -45 degrees from magnetic north, five events. This suggests that some bunching of the data is possible but there

Fig.42: The Bratton quintuplet of July 1983 (photograph by Ian Mrzyglod). Compare with the aerial shot of the same system in Figure 33 (note that in Fig. 42 the angle is too oblique to show up the fine ring interlinking the satellites).

are not enough data for any definite correlation to be established. Totalled together this amounts to 1 in 2.6 as against an expected chance result of 1 in 3.75.

7.4 DEVELOPMENT OF THE AUTHOR'S IDEAS

In 1980 my initial thought, having seen two plain circles near an escarpment, was that an atmospheric vortex was involved. A type of fair-weather whirlwind seemed plausible at first, except that it needed to be a vortex which differed from the usual in that, although external rising currents might be assumed in the normal way, the theoretically-known internal downdraught was abnormally pronounced, at least for the brief period during which the flat bed and outflowing spiral pattern were created. I thought that somehow the proximity of the hill could be part of a specialized vortex-forming scenario[65].

The discovery of five-circle sets in 1983, repeated in 1984 and 1985, confirmed the natural origin of the circles as arising from atmospheric vortices, the implied multiplicity of vortices being not new *per se* to the domain of natural vortices (cf with the familiar sub-vortices of devils and tornadoes)[66]. For the reasons given in Chapter 5 and below it was by then realised that the vortices producing the circles were not some species of the electrostatic *fair-weather* whirlwind after all, so, following the report on the 1984 season, no further reference to them has been made by the author. Instead the circles were understood to be made by some other kind of electrically-active atmospheric vortex of meteorological origin.

In these years all the quintuplets had a big centre circle and four very small ones, all spiralling clockwise (Figure 3, row C, third drawing). Somehow, there must arise a standing-wave interaction coupling the central circle with the outer ones[67]. I had known for twenty years that in field-experiments in the Sahara and New Mexico the electric field of devils (fair-weather whirlwinds) had been measured[28-30]; also that some tornadoes had been documented as electrically superactive with self-luminous, lightning-lit columns and radio-frequency emissions[33]. So it seemed that the circle-circle interaction implied a strong electromagnetic vortex-vortex interaction (Section 5.5). The problem appeared more complex and more important than it had at the beginning. If electrical effects could be so intense as now implied, the circulating current in the primary vortex must be very powerful. This would accord with the inferred brevity of the forces that flatten the corn so effectively. The satellite circles of the 1983 Bratton quintuplet were linked by an extremely narrow arc (as revealed clearly in the air photographs taken by Chris Wood, Figure 33); the same was noted in photographs at Goodworth Clatford 1985. This implied that the arcs could be the path of a stream of circulating ions of air, the narrowness of which recalled the thin-walled sheaths known to exist for waterspouts. Might this mean that the cylindrical walls of tornadoes and waterspouts owed their thinness to a circulation of electric charge, the charges being attached to aerosol dust or cloud or water droplets?

Realising the scientific significance of these discoveries and the hypotheses involving electromagnetism, I decided in summer 1985[68] that for the time being I would limit theoretical comments to extending and clarifying those which I had already discussed in public (these principally involved the search for the dynamic origin of the mechanical forces that create appropriate vortex-spin situations) while nevertheless continuing to share survey details, photographs and past records with any friends wishing to co-operate in a proper scientific spirit.

In order to progress more rapidly many more circles had to be sought each year with the hope that some would be found to which exact dates and times could definitely be assigned. This would help lead to the natal home of the vortices. Although a variation on the theme of summer whirlwind was not tenable in view of the accumulating evidence provided by the quintuplet sets of 1983-1985 (and in 1986 the first ringed-circle sets), a lee effect remained probable for many of the circles that I had so far studied, and so I regarded the effect as an all-the-year-round one.

It was about this time that I received a good report from North Yorkshire of short-lived stationary vortices spinning under cloudy skies in the January snow of 1985[69]. This emphasized the eddy character of some vortices, just as for eddy waterspouts in lakes and coastal waters when close to hills[70,71]. Subsequent events have corroborated this. The probability has increased that in many known situations topography plays a role in producing the vortex which is fundamental to the problem. This may operate through a wake or trailing-vortex disturbance provoked by hill, scarp or rugged-ground circumstances. Whatever the precise nature of the forcing mechanism a vortex tube and/or localized vortex are created which are in a highly charged state, presumably because of the high spin rate and because the local electrostatic field has undergone severe modifications from its normal fair-weather condition. When circumstances allow the vortex tube to be visible it appears as a luminescent pipe extending downwards from the atmospheric region in which the charges are gathered (cf Section 4.7). This is the source of a spinning volume of air which appears to have the properties of a plasma state of matter and which leads ultimately to the circles effect. Moreover, the finding for the first time, in 1986, of circles with an outer annular ring was unambiguous proof of induced ionization. If these rings had made their appearance back in 1980, it would have spared me a vast amount of effort and time. Now we know that numerous rings alternating in direction are ultimately to be expected.

7.5 THE CIRCLES-EFFECT PLASMOID

What is the picture currently held of the circles-effect vortex?

In most instances we envisage an axisymmetric body of fast-spinning air containing an effective but low-density fraction of ionized gas known as plasma. The axis of rotation can be vertical or inclined at some angle to the vertical. In the 'fair-weather whirlwind' parallel, namely the land-devil with the properties of an electrostatic vortex, its raised dust is centrifuged towards the cylindrical exterior. The high dust-density in this region suggests a corresponding high space-density for the charges. The tubular appearance is seen most clearly in the upper reaches of tall devils well clear of the more confused ground region. Therefore a self-luminous tubular structure would be apparent if whirlwind-devils were able to form at night-time. Thermally-induced devils, being the result of solar forcing of air having background angular momentum, are necessarily daytime occurrences, but eddy-whirlwinds and eddy-waterspouts are not so restricted and may be self-luminous at times, which means that they have the potential of being visible at night.

As for the shape of the circles-effect vortex we suppose that as the ion content intensifies, there is an increasing tendency for the interface between ionized volume and the quasi-neutral air beyond to contract its surface area from that of a cylinder or cone towards that of a cigar or sphere in order to minimize its potential energy, while the result of intensifying spin is to modify it further leading to a discoidal appearance. At night a 'ball of light' would most typically be seen.

7.6 GENERALIZED ARGUMENT

The wind vortex is the concentrating force that pumps electrical energy into a specific volume of air, thereby giving rise to the luminous discharge phenomenon. This volume which is axi-symmetric and self-confining, we term the plasma vortex. Depending on the local state of the atmosphere and landscape characteristics it may be short-lived or long-lived, sometimes shooting quickly to the ground, or occasionally hovering or otherwise moving about the locality. Its lifetime depends upon whether it remains within the vortex tube or is ejected from it, and upon its net charge and the direction and magnitude of the local electric field.

The luminescent plasma is constituted of separated charges, the nature of which is open to discussion but which is taken to be a mixed assembly of ions and electrons, with the luminous discharges emanating from the energy of recombination or de-excitation of metastable states. Although quasi-neutral at first, the plasma volume, or plasmoid, after a while comes to acquire a net charge of either sign. When this volume is severed from its energy supply, it is doomed to rapid extinction, a consequence of the classical virial theorem which sets restrictions on the maximum amount of internal energy which can be stored.

The lifetimes of the long-lived plasmas are greatly extended by a continuous supply of fresh charges. These replenish losses suffered through recombination within the plasmoid and through positive-ion and electron currents angled away from it in response to the electric field. However, as the mobility of positive ions is sluggish compared with the faster-moving electrons, *the net charge density remaining in the plasma might be thought soon to become positive* due to the faster rate at which electrons are lost. Therefore for an appropriately-directed local field, a positively-circulating descending current could rotate clockwise and ultimately leave a clockwise imprint upon the crop. However, if some mechanical force is applied (as by the action of 'external' wind movements) which superimposes a temporary counterclockwise action on the entire spinning mass, then the plasmoid suffers two motions, the one at first flattening stalks anticlockwise until the underlying internal clockwise motion reasserts itself. This doubly-impressed motion could explain the observed S-shape patterns as occasionally found in circle beds.

The concept of *positively-charged plasmoids* would be able to explain how plasma vortices could move *contrary to the windflow*. This could apply whether the wind in question is the upward flow of a columnar vortex or is a horizontally-directed windflow. For instance, if, as is known for devil whirlwinds, the local electric field is reversed and points earthwards, then, as Powell and Finkelstein suggested[47] for ball lightning plasmas aided by a non-linear d.c. electric field an electrohydrodynamical force could prevent convective mixing and cause the positively-charged ball to move downwards or against the wind. One may conjecture that the fast-spinning plasma vortex could thus be attracted to the ground, either making a violent or explosive impact (as exposed by a starburst or a crater) or creating the spiral form of the circles effect. Alternatively, it may find itself being repelled as the ground is neared if charges of the same sign are strongly enough represented there, and create for the vortex ball a hovering situation which could lead to a repulsion and promote a return skywards.

What is the source of the internal radiation?

We have no certain evidence from our circles studies regarding heating effects at the time of plasma vortex descent. A browning or withering appearance rarely noted may just as well have been the result of trampling caused by subsequent investigators. From the literature we find that a few vortices (devils and tornadoes) and balls of light have been noted to be accompanied by warm air currents. Even ball lightning, for all its incandescence, is considered to be a comparatively low-heat phenomenon. Certainly, we think that the circles-effect vortices represent a mainly cool discharge. It is probably an atmospheric-pressure type of glow discharge of the kind produced artificially by Powell and Finkelstein[47] although by an entirely different process. That is to say, not much develops in the way of disassociation of molecules; it is rather the consequence of their excitation into electron-ion pairs by the Townsend avalanche-effect. The visible and non-visible radiations are emitted as excited molecules return to ground states from temporary metastable states.

Powell and Finkelstein achieved their experimental success by focussing radio-frequency energy to create ball-lightning type plasmas. Although the excitation source from within the atmosphere for our plasma vortices is not known, and the possibility of some natural direct-current source may be forthcoming, we have some visual reports which suggest that the balls of light we are studying may be pulsed. Besides this, we know that they produce radio-frequency noise on the radio-communication bands and that they upset television transmissions. Moreover, there is the evidence of the circles's rings and satellites which if explicable by a standing-wave hypothesis (Sections 5.5, 7.7) bears witness to oscillatory flow (and thereby counts against plain electrostatic vorticity as in the common whirlwind of fair-weather origin). Therefore, the electrical behaviour of our vortex differs in several ways from that of the common devils, especially as the latter have never been reported to have concentric outer sheaths or to produce pulsed electromagnetic effects like tornadoes and waterspouts do.

7.7 STANDING WAVES

Is the pulsing a product of the fast-spinning vortex and its piping along the vortex tube? The observed balls of light might be related to an oscillating electromagnetic field formed within the cylindrical cavity that is the vortex tube. Whatever the dynamics may be, the plasma ball itself, fast-spinning and self-contained, seems to create its own fields and natural radio-frequency waves.

Upon approaching the ground, especially if it is a good conducting surface (because it is wet, say), the plasma's electromagnetic wave radiation could undergo reflection and encourage a standing-wave system. Antinodes and nodes would appear at intervals whose geometrical positions and sizes are determined by local conditions and wavelength properties, the maximum field intensities developing at the antinodes. Kapitsa studied the ball-lightning problem in this connection in terms of interactions between plasmoids and electromagnetic field oscillations which occur when a resonance develops between wavelength and plasma diameter[45]. Might similar forces give rise to plasma-vortex satellites, these being the optimum locations where plasma gathers via an electric field-resonance condition? The narrow rings linking satellites (Section 5.5) are generated by ions which circulate until trapped in small plasma clouds at the appropriate points. The energy rises rapidly and the increasing field further cascades local ionization processes. The sense of rotation depends on the net ion species dominating the space-charge-density; a net positive-ion circulation may mean clockwise rotation while circulating negative charges could lead to anticlockwise rings and possibly satellites.

Although Kapitsa's focussed electromagnetic-wave resonance theory is not applicable without appreciable modification it is interesting to note that if we use his condition for resonance – viz. that the ball diameter d is coupled to the absorbed wavelength L by the condition that d equals or is greater than L/3.65 – then for the known satellite-diameter range of three to ten metres, a wavelength range of 3 MHz to 900 kHz is implied, which seems to embrace the right orders of magnitude for the radio-frequency noise detected by radio and television.

Single rings around single circles often rotate in a sense opposite to that of the interior. This seems to imply a windflow resulting from an induced current of opposite sign. The process may be similar in those other sheathed vortices which are known as waterspouts. In any event, the point remains valid that for our crop-ring cases (as for circle-perimeters) a critical force is required to blow down the stalks. As the momentum of flowing charged particles crosses a threshold level (mass times critical speed), one passes from a state with fallen stalks to undamaged stalks, sometimes in a matter of a few millimetres measured radially. Benedicks's surface-tension idea would further restrict the shear windfield to a narrow interval of space.

Regarding the differently-coloured exteriors, or halo effect, sometimes noted for ball-of-light plasmas (e.g. as in Section 6.5), these may result from a secondary electron flow from the surrounding atmosphere returning to the vortex, causing in their turn attendant molecular excitations and light emissions.

Some remarks on the constitution of air are called for. Besides its fundamental list of active and inert gases dominated by nitrogen and oxygen, there are highly variable quantities of carbon dioxide, water vapour and dust particles, all of which can play a crucial role in charge and discharge processes. We shall not go into this here, save to say that the dust thrown up by the whirlwind species known as land-devils is essential for their electrostatic-field development, as it is for dust-storms. After measuring the electrical properties of a land-devil in New Mexico (1964) Crozier studied and reported on a further seventeen devils, negative potential-gradients being found for them all. This is a total reversal of the normal fair-weather field[29,30]. Devils seem to owe their static electrification to the upward spiral agitation of particulate matter to which charges are attracted by ill-understood tribo-electric processes[32].

Automobiles may likewise be a source of particulate matter both on account of raised dust and exhaust products, besides being a 'warm' centre for a local thermal plume. Electrostatic charges accumulate on cars, as on helicopters, by virtue of their carriers, particles of blown dust. A plasma vortex may find itself attracted thus, and its life extended, when in the proximity of a vehicle. This could explain the several known occasions when ball-of-light phenomena appear to have acquired and maintained some affinity for cars[51] (cf also the cases of Chapter 6.5, 6.7, 6.8). Or looked at the other way, could it be due to ions induced or leaked from the field of a plasma vortex that a car's electrical and ignition systems come to get upset?

Lastly, there is possibly the electrification of fast-spinning condensed water drops to consider in view of the laboratory work of Lavan and Frejer[72]. Although the conditions of this experiment cannot be compared directly with atmospheric vortices, one is led to suggest that what appears, as regards the charge distribution, recombination rate, etc (and hence brightness, colour, induced charge distributions, heat, and sound) of the low-density plasma gas, may depend on the dust and water content (air humidity) of the air and its distribution. Similarities of the constitution of the atmosphere over big distances might then explain why, when there is an outbreak of vortices leading to circle formation, patterns of a particular type are sometimes widespread (e.g. there were numerous quintuplets in July 1985, three systems with the rare contra-rotation types with rings in July 1986, two or three triangular triplets dated to June 1988, etc).

7.8 A SOLUTION FOR OTHER PROBLEMS?

As we draw to the close of this report we wish to mention one of the conclusions of the Condon inquiry set up by the U.S. government in the 1960's as a scientific study into what is commonly termed 'unidentified flying objects'. 117 cases were assessed in this report, concerning which the conclusion was reached that "as 70% of the cases were identified nothing of scientific value would come of further studies". The implication latent in this statement is that if enough information had been available the other 30% might have been identified too[73]. However, a quick check of these unsolved cases reveals that some of them look to be fine examples of the plasma vortices we have been investigating. This may mean that if a follow-up study had been conducted in the Condon-cited "important areas of atmospheric optics, including radiowave propagation, and of atmospheric electricity" at even a modest university or government research level it might have led to the discoveries reported by the present author.

We have space to indicate two of these cases briefly.

Case 10 (ref. 73, pp 277-280). Winter 1966, South Central USA. "A pulsating reddish light seen below treetop level from a highway at night became brilliant white briefly, then resumed its earlier character". It pulsated regularly, ranging from dull red to bright orange with a period of about two seconds. An illumination of several hundred megawatts was estimated by the principle witness, a nuclear physicist, for the light at the peak of its brilliance on what was a dark, rainy night. "Although the report did not relate specifically to an UFO, the qualifications of the principal witness, the similarity of the reported incident to many UFO reports, and the possibility of recurrence or observable effects of heat, all appeared to justify a field investigation".

Case 38 (ref. 73, pp 375-379): Fall 1967, North Eastern U.S.A. A 55-year-old woman "stated that she had observed a large glowing light behind her house. The next morning, she found a 'saucer nest' in the cattails where she had seen the light".

It was said that the vegetation damage in a small swamp was in the form of a 30-ft diameter area where "cattails had been squashed down and found to lie in a clock-wise spiral pattern". Unfortunately, the two investigators from the Condon team arrived several weeks after the event which was too late to assess the damage in the swamp. The woman who made this report is employed in local government service, and impressed the interviewers as sincere and intelligent.

As regards the problem of unidentified aerial phenomena as a whole we recognise along with Dr J. Allen Hynek that "there exists a subset of UFO reports of high strangeness and high witness credibility for which no-one . . . has been able to ascribe a viable explanation" (AIAA 13th Aerospace Sciences Meeting, Pasadena, January 1975). It may be that the explanations offered in this book will go some way to relieving a major part of one such subset of its strangeness.

Lastly, mentioned briefly in the Condon Report in a chapter written by Martin D. Altschuler are suggestions made in 1966 by Philip J. Klass "that ball lightning may occur under many situations, and consequently may be the cause of many unusual UFO sightings". I point this out although I have not had access to Klass's work[74-75].

7.9 CONCLUDING REMARKS AND A LOOK TO THE FUTURE

Surveys and eye-witness reports of spiral-centred circles formed in crops have been analysed for the information they provide on the nature of the atmospheric vortices which create them. Evidence for concomitant acoustic, luminous and radio-frequency electromagnetic effects has been assessed and the conclusion drawn that the air of the spinning vortices which blows down the crop is ionized. It seems that this electrically-charged volume could be described as a low-density plasma which is probably often ball-shaped and has some affinities with ball lightning. It is inferred that high rotational speeds modify the shape into a flattened spheroidal or discoidal form, and that a continuous electrical discharge illuminates it. Life-times are considerably longer than for ball lightning because losses from discharge effects due to recombination and leakage are balanced by inputs piped along the conducting channel of the supporting columnar vortex. The assembly of observations may account for some of the sightings of transient aerial phenomena reported by the public and popularly termed flying saucers or unidentified flying objects. An alternative possibility is that the vortices have an electrostatic origin rather than a plasma one.

Our explanation for the circles effect uses no more than the laws of physics and the properties of the atmosphere. It turns out that an atmospheric effect which has been missed by previous physicists and meteorologists is at the root of the solution. One does not have to resort to *ad hoc* hypotheses drawn from the pseudo-scientific and paranormal world.

Our work is in the pioneering stage. The new facts appearing each year are susceptible of modifying the ideas we have put forward. The explanations advanced at this stage are hardly likely to explain everything in any case because we suspect that there could be more than one species of circle-making vortex involved, but the work should certainly provide a good forum for discussion and encouragement for grant-aided research. We cannot help but point out that the solution as proposed here will have far-reaching consequences for low-altitude aircraft flight safety (clear-air turbulence), radio-communications (r.f. band interference, radar angels, etc), an improved understanding of atmosphere dynamics, and a better appreciation of what is known as the 'U.F.O. problem'.

Circumstantial evidence already to hand suggests that aircraft crashes in the vicinity of circle-prone landscapes is anomalously high. For example the former R.A.F. airfield at Yatesbury, Wiltshire (near Windmill Hill, the Cherhill escarpment and Beckhampton Down) suffered a seemingly anomalous high number of aircraft accidents from unknown or wind-related causes during its long operational period (from the First World War until its closure in the 1960's). Governments who regard such matters as important should be concerned with researching the origins of these problems. Not only are low-flying military aeroplanes at risk, but also private and commercial light aircraft, helicopters and microlights.

Details of the parent vortex system and the 'electrified ball' that ultimately lead to the ground traces are far from complete chiefly because not enough is known observationally, but now that some of the principles are understood we may direct our resources in the most profitable directions. Yet if we merely stand and wait for fresh clues to turn up at random, many decades may pass without much progress because the effect is uncommon, despite the large number of relevant events that we uncover retrospectively each year. Only three eye-witness accounts of circles in the process of formation have reached us yet (plus a possible fourth); they were all unplanned, chance sightings. Good visual descriptions are needed, especially in combination with photographic and video data. To this end the author is prepared to organize teams of spotters, who will need to be equipped with photographic and instrumental recording apparatus, because the best sites need to be monitored efficiently. With an ever-improving understanding of the local weather processes we should be able to oversee sites continuously whenever weather conditions for producing the circles effect look promising. So, let us hope for a scientifically-instrumented sighting in the near future!

It is encouraging to approach this challenge with two axioms in mind: *'Science advances by the unexpected happening',* and *'Chance favours the mind that is prepared'.*

Fig.43: Guardian of so many secrets, the White Horse gazes down on Bratton's circle-damaged fields.

REFERENCES

1. G. T. MEADEN, J. Meteorology, vol.6, 76-80, 1981; vol.7, 45-49, 1982; vol.8, 11-19, 216-217, 1983; vol.9, 137-146, 1984; vol.10, 73-80, 1985; vol.11, 152-153, 1986; vol.12, 44-51, 210-211, 1987; vol.13, 203-212, 290, 305-310, 1988; vol.14, 83-85, 1989; Weather, vol.44, 2-10, 1989.

2. C. P. FULLER, A sample survey of the incidence of geometrically-shaped crop damage. 40 pp. BUFORA, 1988 (Burgess Hill, Sussex).

3. C. ANDREWS. J. Meteorology, vol.12, 48-51, 1987; Meaden, ibid. 44-48.

4. S. YAMAGUCHI and N. NAMIKI. Magazine article, 1988 (in Japanese).

5. ANON. 1880. A curious phenomenon. Sci. Amer. vol.43, 25 (reprinted by W. R. Corliss. Handbook of Natural Phenomena. The Scourcebook Project, Glen Arm, Md U.S.A. 1977).

6. D. LARDNER. Popular geology and popular physics 1856.

7. M. BELL, in Meaden, J. Meteorology vol.10, 73-80, 1985; also his testimony in the BBC film shown in October 1988.

8. A. SHUTTLEWOOD in the magazine Now!, 29 August 1988, reprinted in J. Met. vol.9, 137-146, 1984.

9. G. T. MEADEN, Eyewitness account of a spiral-circle at Westbury, Wiltshire, J. Meteorology, vol.14, 265-270, July/August 1989.

10. Maximum temperature at Bradford-on-Avon was 11.4 deg. C. Dull sunless day; rainy periods from 12 GMT for much of the afternoon and evening; overcast or cloudy night, then further rain after dawn; 24-hour rainfall total 3.5mm.

11. G. T. MEADEN, Two spiral-circles, and the descending vortex which hit a garage. J. Meteorology, vol.15 (1990) to be published.

12. G. T. MEADEN, British tornadoes of the 1960's: Part 2 1963-64. J. Meteorology, vol.5, 173-184, 1980.

13. A. SHUTTLEWOOD. The Warminster Mystery. N. Spearman, London. 1967.

14. G. T. MEADEN. The vortices of vapour seen near Avebury, Wiltshire, above a wheatfield on 16 June 1988. J. Meteorology, 13, 305-310, 1988.

15. G. T. MEADEN. A vortex of vapour seen above the Carron Forest in Scotland on 7 May 1983. J. Meteorology 13, 310-311, 1988.

16. A. SHUTTLEWOOD. UFOs – Key to the New Age. pp 57-58.

17. A. SHUTTLEWOOD. More UFOs over Warminster. pp 115-116.

18. W. I. ARABADJI. J. Geophys. Research, vol.81, 6455-56, 1976.

19. G. J. JENKINS, P. J. MASON, W. H. MOORES and R. I. SYKES. Measurements of the flow structure around Ailsa Craig, a steep, three-dimensional, isolated hill. Quart. J. Roy. Met. Soc. vol.107, 833-851, 1981.

20. N. J. COOK, B. H. COULSON and W. McKAY. Wind conditions around the Rock of Gibralter. J. Ind. Aerodyn, vol.2, 289-309, 1978.

21. In private correspondence Dr Snow has proposed ideas by which each plain circle documents, in some integrated sense, the spin-up of a columnar vortex. A concentrated core aloft, resulting from convergence and stretching of vortices, first builds downwards till it interacts with the surface. Vortex breakdown then ensues, commencing aloft, and extending groundwards to create a circle of expanding diameter, having possibly begun the crop-damage process via a ring of very small diameter.

22. G. T. MEADEN. Advances in the understanding of whirlwind spiral patterns in cereal fields (1984 Season). J. Meteorology, vol.11, 152-153, 1985.

23. J. M. HEIGHES. Funnel cloud observations downwind from a chimney. Weather, vol.25, 289-290, 1970.

24. G. T. MEADEN. The mystery of spiral-circle ground patterns in crops made by a natural atmospheric-vortex phenomenon. Proc. Second TORRO Conference, Oxford, June 1988. J. Meteorology, vol.13, 202-212, 1988.

25. F. H. LUDLAM. Clouds and Storms. Pennsylvania State University Press, 1980. pp 369-370 et seq.

26. P. DELGADO. Private communication. See also Flying Saucer Review, vol.32, November 1987, pp 5-9.

27. 36 hours earlier the wind was nearer north-west, perhaps north-north-west or north for a while, which would set the wind bluff to the escarpment.

28. G. D. FREIER. The electric field of a large dust devil. J. Geophys. Research, vol.65, 3504, 1960.

29. W. D. CROZIER. The electric field of a New Mexico dust devil. ibid vol.69. 5427-5429, 1964.

30. W. D. CROZIER. Dust devil properties. ibid. vol.75, 4583-5, 1970.

31. W. E. BRADLEY and R. G. SEMONIN. Airborne electrical measurements in dust whirls. J. Atmos. Sciences, vol.20, 622-623, 1963.

32. A. K. KAMRA. Effect of wind on atmospheric electric field. J. Atmos. Terr. Phys. 1969.

33. B. VONNEGUT. Electrical theory of tornadoes. J. Geophys, vol.65, 203-212, 1960.

34. F. C. MONTGOMERY. Tornadoes at Blackwell, Okla., May 25, 1955. Mon. Wea. Rev. vol.83, 109, 1955; Weatherwise, vol.9, 97, 101 (1955).

35. G. T. MEADEN. British tornadoes and waterspouts of the 1960's. Part 1: 1960-62. J. Meteorology vol.5, 151-2, 1960; also M. W. Rowe under ref. 37.

36. BEESLEY. Met. Mag. vol.8, 149-154 and 167, 1873.

37. M. W. ROWE. The earliest documented tornado in the British Isles: Rosdalla, Co. Westmeath, Eire., April 1054. J. Meteorology. vol.14, 86-90, 1989.

38. O. H. VAUGHAN and B. VONNEGUT. Luminous electrical phenomena associated with nocturnal tornadoes in Huntsville, Alabama, 3 April 1974. Bull. Amer. Met. Soc. vol.57, 1220-4, 1976.

39. H. L. JONES. A sferic method of tornado identification and tracking. Bull. Amer. Met Soc. vol.32, 380-385, 1951.

40. H. L. JONES. The tornado pulse generator. Weatherwise, vol.18, 78-79, 1955 (reprinted by Corliss, pp 345-6 of ref.5.

41. ANON. in Lumieres dans la nuit. 1976; see also J. Meteorology vol.14, 84-85, 1989.

42. V.-J. BALLESTER OLMOS, priv. communication, report entitled 'Vento de furacao'. Witness, José Ferreira Nabais.

43. B. VONNEGUT and J. R. WEYER. Luminous phenomena in nocturnal tornadoes. Science, vol.153, 1213-1220, 1966.

44. ROY CRAIG, Chapter 4, 97-108, of Condon report, ref 73.

45. P. L. KAPITSA. The nature of ball lightning. Doklady Akad. NAUK, SSSR, vol.101, 245-248, 1955 (English transl. in W. Gerbes and E. Dewan, Physik, Bl., vol.1, 1958).

46. R. S. SCORER, private communication.

47. J. R. POWELL and D. FINKELSTEIN. Structure of ball lightning, in Advances in Geophysics, H. E. Landsberg and J. Van Miegham (ed). Academic Press, New York, vol.13, 141, 1969. Rev. Geophys. 1969.

48. M. STENHOFF. A survey of ball lightning. J. Meteorology, vol.13, 197-203, 1988.

49. Ref.13, pp 93-94.

50. ibid.

51. G. FALLA. Vehicle interference project (Ed. C. F. Lockwood and A. R. Pace). B.U.F.O.R.A. Report 1979.

52. JOHN TURNER. Private communication.

53. Devizes and Wiltshire Gazette, p 3, of 2 July 1857 issue.

54. Ref.13, pp 27-29.

55. C. BENEDICKS. Theory of the lightning balls and its application to the atmospheric phenomenon called flying saucers. Arkiv f. Physik, vol.2, p.1, 1954.

56. G. T. MEADEN. A study of the effect of aircraft trailing vortices upon a cereal-field near an airport. J. Meteorology, vol.14, 9-17, 1989.

57. P. DELGADO. Mystery swirled rings in England, 1985. Flying Saucer Review, vol.13, no 5, p 12, July 1986.

58. Notwithstanding this, short straight lines (under 5-10km) could demarcate the 'lines of separation' familiar to the boundary meteorologist for hill-lee situations.

59. BBC Film, 'Running rings round Arthur', October 1988.

60. P. DEVEREUX, P. McCARTNEY and D. ROBINS. Bringing UFO's down to earth. New Scientist, London, 1 September 1983.

61. P. DELGADO. 1986 mystery circles: the final summary. Flying Saucer Review. vol.32, no 6, p. 5, of pp 5-9, Nov 1987.

62. ibid. p. 9.

63. C. ANDREWS. Circles in the corn: Strong evidence of a UFO connection. Flying Saucer Review, vol.32, no 6, 9-13, 1987.

64. C. ANDREWS. Circular evidence. MUFON UFO Journal, no 243, pp 11-13, July 1988. The new book *Circular evidence* by Delgado and Andrews provides *no proof* regarding the action of an "intelligent" force after all. Instead, these authors erroneously state that the force is 'silent', 'total darkness operating', 'weather-condition free', 'topographically conditionless', etc (p.158), and that 'it must have no lights or illumination associated with it'. Any idea of electromagnetism is firmly rejected too.

    Another book published in July 1989 is *Controversy of the circles* by P. Fuller and J. Randles. This book is especially useful for the details it provides of the history of circles research in Britain 1980-1988 from the point of view of BUFORA (37 Heathbank Road, Stockport, SK3 0UP, England).

65. G. T. MEADEN. Articles in J. Meteorology, vol.6, 76-80, 1981; 7, 45-49, 1982; and 8, 11-19, 1983.

66. Ibid. 9, 137-146, 1984; 10, 73-80, 1985; 11, 152-153, 1986.

67. G. T. MEADEN. ibid. vol.9, p. 143, 1984; vol.13, 209, 1988.

68. G. T. MEADEN. Quintuplet circle formation in 1985. ibid. vol.11, pp 152-153, 1986.

69. M. J. CINDEREY. Stationary wind-devils in the January snow in North Yorkshire. ibid., vol.10, p 339, 1985.

70. J. G. HOLBOURNE. The Foula whirlwinds known as flans. ibid., vol.10, 300-301, 1985.

71. G. T. MEADEN. Eddy whirlwinds, waterspouts and tornadoes. Waterspouts on Rydal Water. ibid. 10, 301-302, 1985.

72. Z. LAVAN and A. A. FREJER. Luminescence in supersonic swirling flows. J. Fluid Mech. vol.23, 173, 1965.

73. E. U. CONDON. Scientific study of unidentified flying objects. Bantam Books, New York, 1969.

74. M. D. ALTSCHULER. Chapter 7, in ref.73.

75. P. J. KLASS. Flying saucers identified. Random House, New York, 1968.

Ancillary note on publications regarding the circles effect: there are several additional papers, and four books by G. T. Meaden which are completed and will be published in due course.

GLOSSARY

BALL LIGHTNING. A small globular ball of light formed in the atmosphere often in thundery conditions. Diameters are mostly reported as smaller than 0.4 - 0.5 metre. The lifetime is short, chiefly less than a couple of seconds, rarely above five seconds. Its electrical constitution is unknown but a cool plasma has been inferred to explain many cases, the energy thought to be stored in metastable molecularly-excited levels.

BALLS OF LIGHT. A term used in this book to distinguish self-illuminated quasi-spherical light-forms from ball lightning by their greater size and their capacity for much longer life.

CIRCLES EFFECT. The occurrence of circular-symmetric patterns formed in crops on the ground by descent of an atmospheric vortex which we call the 'circles-effect vortex'.

CIRCLES-EFFECT VORTEX. The name given to the vortex that creates the circles effect in crops or on the ground. It is an axi-symmetric body of fast-spinning air thought to contain a significant fraction of ionized gas which may be in the plasma state.

ELECTRICAL DISCHARGE. De-excitation of excited air molecules and atoms (see under next heading) accompanied by effects of light, sound and radio-frequency energy (and less noticeably heat).

EXCITATION OF AIR MOLECULES. Air molecules can be excited into temporary metastable states as electron-ion pairs. They emit visible and non-visible radiation as they return to their ground states in a process called electrical discharge.

FAIR-WEATHER FIELD. The earth's average electric field near sea-level in fair weather is positive at ca 130 volts per metre directed downwards. It is maintained by the occurrence of thunderstorms across the entire world.

GEOSTROPHIC WIND. Airflow generated by the large-scale pressure gradients associated with the mobile distribution of depressions and anticyclones.

ION. An ion is a charged atom or molecule, one which has gained or lost an electron and has thereby acquired electric charge.

IONIZATION is the process of exciting atoms or molecules to become ions.

LAND DEVIL OR WHIRLWIND. The fair-weather whirlwind known as a land-devil or dust-devil when it is seen levitating dust and dirt from fields is formed from a rotating thermal or plume of buoyant warm air. By their capacity to levitate highly-electrified dust particles these whirlwinds are electrostatic vortices and the self-creators of negative electric fields, opposite in sign to the fair-weather field.

PLASMA. If a gas acquires sufficient ions or electrons that its physical properties are affected, it is called plasma. In this book we used the word to describe air in a partially-ionized state.

PLASMOID. Used to denote a body of plasma, in this book a spinning plasma.

TORNADO. The bad-weather whirlwind associated with the descent of a funnel-cloud from thundery clouds or line squalls.

T.O.R.R.O. The Tornado and Storm Research Organization.

VORTEX. The rapid spinning of particles of matter about an axis.

WATERSPOUT. A natural atmospheric vortex equivalent to a tornado spout or devil acting over a water surface instead of land.

WHIRLWIND. This is strictly the general name used to describe any mesoscale or small vortex formed naturally in the atmosphere. Many laymen use it for the fair-weather whirlwind, and some apply it instead of the preferred word 'tornado' for the bad-weather whirlwind.

WIND. The movement of air caused by a pressure gradient, a temperature gradient, or electromagnetic forces acting on ionized air.

C.E.R.E.S. – AND THE VORTEX-CIRCLE PROBLEM

WORLD DATA-BANK AND RESEARCH TEAMS

CERES, the *Circles Effect Research Unit* of the Tornado and Storm Research Organisation (TORRO), is a privately-funded, investigative body which researches the intriguing, worldwide problem of vortices that strike circular-symmetric damage patterns into cornfields. Additional help from enthusiasts who can serve as spotters and local investigators in Britain or the rest of the world are welcome. Besides reporting on the circles themselves volunteers may wish to take part in co-ordinated watches which have the purpose of monitoring potential sites night and day in order to capture on film and video-tape the formation sequence of the various species of circle-sets and the electromagnetic spinning systems which create them.

This challenging research programme began in a small way in 1980 when the author first learnt of circles in his locality, and has since grown into a project of formidable scientific importance having a tremendous popular appeal. Field investigations start in May when the crops are mature enough to submit to permanent damage when struck by the vortex, and they continue until harvest time. The spinning vortex, besides marking cereal crops and other vegetation types, leaves circular traces in earth, sand, snow and frost-covered grass, sometimes scouring or blasting circular hollows into soft ground. These studies are also part of CERES's research programme because the ultimate aim is to understand the plasma vortex at the heart of the problem. Hence, we are just as interested to learn of any localized occurrences in which short-lived non-tornadic gyratory forces appear to have arrived from a skyward direction, and caused unusual damage or other effects to buildings, gardens, automobiles, animals and people. Such happenings can occur at night as well as by day, and in the winter too, for this is a problem that is amenable to study the whole year round if witnesses or susceptible material chance to be present. We are particularly anxious to expand our studies of associated electromagnetic phenomena at all seasons, having already amassed a quantity of direct evidence and a vast amount of circumstantial evidence which link the circles-effect vortex to optical and electrical manifestations having affinities with the ball lightning phenomenon.

Consequently, in order to assemble into a single archive every scrap of information that might be relevant to the subject, an *international data bank* has been established for the collection of data and photographs not only on the primary question of the circles effect but on ancillary vortex-related phenomena which involve luminosity (especially low, hovering, spinning, pulsating, and descending lights or balls-of-light), electrical effects (interference to radio-communications, television, vehicle performance), and unusual noises (humming, whining, whistling, crackling, etc).

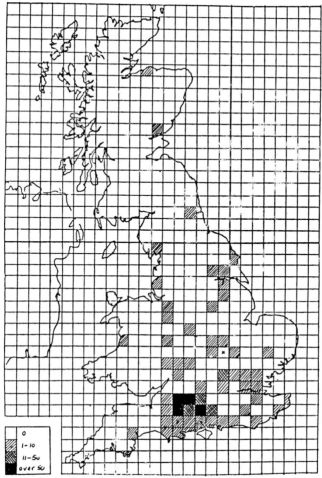

Fig.44: England and Wales have been divided into squares 25km x 25km on the national grid system to show those areas (shaded) for which reports of the circles effect have been received (updated to January 1990). The sites of the Charlton circular crater (in a potato field) and the Sharnbrook circular blast (in a brussels-sprouts field) are indicated by crosses. We need spotters to help us fill in the squares!

Readers who can provide any information are invited to get in touch with the author as soon as possible, including those who feel they could act as spotters and investigators of crop circles *anywhere in Britain or the rest of the world.* Do not be discouraged if you have never heard of crop-circles in your region. We should stress that the main reasons why the circles proliferate in central southern England are partly because it is a crop-growing area with undulating countryside and hills but largely because my friends and I have been searching so hard. This makes us confident that other crop-growing counties *with similar topography* have such phenomena too. Figure 44 indicates those parts of England and Wales for which crop-circle effects have been

106

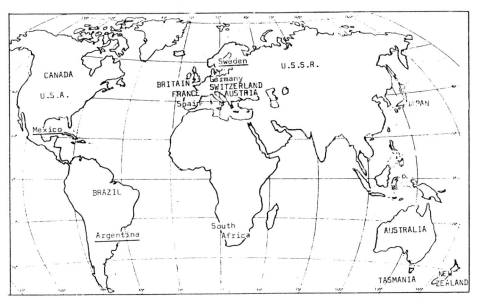

Fig.45: World map showing countries for which evidence of circles-effect vortices is known. For countries marked by capitals we have reports of spiral or radial circles in crops or other vegetation; those underlined refer more generally to reports of circular damage areas in association with vortex phenomena, while the remainder refer to other forms of circular trace in connection with circles-effect vortices (such as eye-witness accounts of spinning aerial phenomena and hollow creation).

reported. A similar map if drawn for known incidents of low-level ball-of-light phenomena would certainly cover the majority of these 25-kilometre grid squares, but with a time spread covering the twelve months of the year rather than the three or four months of later spring and summer.

On the world scale we are confident that many other countries regularly suffer the same vortex-phenomena as does Britain. When 1980 began, the author knew of no swirled spiral-circles for any part of the world, including Britain. The research discipline did not exist, and yet the circles were there all the time, unknown to the busy scientist, their importance unrecognized by the hard-working farmer. Now we have four hundred circles, with most of the continents represented (Figure 45), and pre-1980 cases are being added all the time. Whereas most of these are single circles, a report of rings for 1960 (from Gloucestershire) and photographs of a 1977 double-ringed circle (Northamptonshire) and a 1978 quintuplet (Hampshire) have come to light. In fact, of the pre-1980 events currently to hand a fair percentage (20%) are not British at all.

So be encouraged to search your own part of the world for examples of this marvellous phenomenon, and write to Dr Terence Meaden, CERES, at the publishers address 54 Frome Road, Bradford-on-Avon, Wiltshire, BA15 1LD, for further information (telephone 02216 2482, fax 02216 5601).

Addendum

MESO-FRONTS AND THE CIRCLES EFFECT

The author has recently secured evidence of circle formation on the lee side of a hill in connection with the passage of a slow-moving, weak cold front. This understandable correlation raises the likelihood that the gravity current-flow and horizontal roll-vortices of slow-moving meso-fronts such as sea-breeze fronts may behave similarly, and be the reason for the relatively high frequency of circles on or close to the undulating downs of Southern England where deep inland penetration of maritime air along wide frontal belts develops several times a year in the summer months. The difference in the distance from the south coast for Winchester (30km) and Westbury (60km) can explain the tendency for the circle season to begin earlier in the Winchester-Cheesefoot region of Hampshire (usually June, but sometimes May, with a continuation into September) than in the Westbury escarpment area of Wiltshire (where, for example, the whole activity in 1987 was in late July and August), and why the time of circle formation is sometimes late in the day or even after dark (ref J. E. Simpson, Inland penetration of sea-breeze fronts. *Quart. J. Roy. Meteorol. Soc.* vol. 103, 47-76, 1977). We further propose that as fronts progress northwards or north-north-westwards against opposing gradient winds (geostrophic winds) they may trigger the circles effect beneath the north-facing or N.W.-facing scarp of the Bratton-Westbury-Warminster area, in what had until then been a windward situation for the escarpment (note how this supplements and extends our discussion of page 44). The same suggestion could account for sequential outbreaks of circles involving several sites, some possibly linearly disposed. In short, we are saying that plasma-vortex development is favoured, whether it happens by day or at night, by rising-wind or gust-front interactions (from whatever source) with a pre-existing stable airmass and that on quiet clear nights the latter is the humid, dense layer beneath an inversion.

These remarks should be helpful in permitting us to forecast, for the first time, some of the occasions when plasma vortices and their circular ground traces may occur, and for which purpose monitoring by radar-echo methods would be an advantageous complement to direct observations.

UP-TO-DATE REPORTS ON THE CIRCLES EFFECT AND ITS MYSTERIES

Readers wishing to be acquainted with the latest advances in research on the circles effect and its origins may be interested in subscribing to the *Journal of Meteorology* in which results and papers are published in almost every issue. Subscription rates for this magazine which appears ten times a year are available from the publishers of this book, Artetech Publishing Company.

LATEST NEWS ON CIRCLES RESEARCH

Considerable progress was made in circles research during the summer of 1989. Formation dates at several of the circle sites were known exactly (and the associated weather conditions as well), new circle patterns were discovered, two circle-making plasma balls were sighted descending into wheatfields, and useful theoretical progress was effected. The total number of circles known for 1989 was 300, of which 230 were found in Wiltshire, 16 in Buckinghamshire, 13 in Dorsetshire, 8 in Hertfordshire, 7 in Hampshire, 4 in Devonshire, and 4 in Gloucestershire. There were three in Kent, two each in the counties of Tayside, Berks, and Essex, and one each in Avon, Shropshire, Stafford, Suffolk, Cambridge, Leicester, Notts, and North Humberside. Circles were found in wheat, barley, oats, rapeseed, and tick beans (cattle beans). One circle, about 8 metres in diameter, was incomplete because it overlapped a roadway.

The big total of 300, from 19 counties, is partly the result of increased public awareness, partly due to an increase in flying hours spent searching for circles and partly because so many (about 72) seemed to be associated with a jumbo daytime-outbreak on 9th May when a weak cold front struggled southwards in essentially anticyclonic conditions.

One of the theoretically-important events of 1989 was the quintuplet circle formation east of Aylesbury in July. This 5-circle pattern appeared on a level site *downwind* of a hill-spur of the Chilterns six kilometres to the south-east. These circles are important for demonstrating how far from the creator-hill circles-effect vortices may develop (cf p.38). When told of this case, Paul Fuller informed the author that not far from Aylesbury, at the village of Tringford, there had been a well-investigated ball-of-light event on 9 February 1962 in which a huge luminous ball descended to road level, interfered with the performance of a vehicle, and 'brushed' frost from trees as it departed. Reference to weather charts for that occasion showed that the wind direction (south-west) corresponded with the compass bearing of the nearest part of the Chilterns four kilometres distant.

At Bratton/Westbury (West Wiltshire) circles formed at night on 19 July 1989 in a south-west wind between one and two kilometres from the creator-hillspur to the south-west. The biggest circle (which was anticlockwise) had a diameter of 26 metres. Later in July and early August even bigger circles were formed in north-central Wiltshire. These were clockwise single-ringed circles with main-circle diameters of 32 metres (105 feet). Elsewhere – this time in Avon County – the smallest ringed circle known to us was discovered. It had an internal diameter of four metres and a ring diameter of six metres. In Tayside, Scotland, the formation of a circle was witnessed in late August.

On three occasions in 1989 a clockwise circle was found with a clockwise ring around it. Each time, subsidiary evidence suggested that between circle and ring there existed an additional, concentric but effectively-invisible ring directed in the opposite sense to the others. Also in central Wiltshire a triple-ringed circle occurred, the rings alternating in the usual fashion. Altogether in 1989 fifteen circle sets based on the quintuplet design were discovered. One of these was modified as an unusual septuplet and another as a nonuplet. In addition, three others out of the 15 had extra circles which gave these patterns a 'cruciform' appearance (cf example on the front cover).

Two of the circles discovered in South Wiltshire by ace-spotter/pilot and photographer Mr F. C. Taylor were remarkable for their complex, overlapping, concentric-ring character. One had a curious quadranted symmetry. Another pilot, aerial archaeologist James Pickering of Leicestershire, reported an amazing species of circle from Staffordshire which was subsequently visited by CERES investigator David Reynolds. This unusual circle gave the impression that a plasma ring-vortex may have 'exploded' above the crop canopy (a luminous form had been noticed by the farmer over the field in the night).

On two other occasions, well viewed by witnesses, circles definitely formed in the presence of glowing balls of light. In one of these (in Wiltshire) a huge orange-coloured ball was seen to sink into a wheatfield and extinguish itself. Next morning a 15-metre ringed circle was found at that spot. The other happened in the middle of the night in Kent. A great ball, described as 'a spiralling vortex of light' which made a loud humming noise, descended into a wheatfield and vanished. This was watched by two young men who immediately investigated by the light of the moon and found an 18-m diameter circle. A report has been prepared by Paul Harris.

One morning at Woolstone in Gloucestershire *J. Meteorology* subscriber Michael Rawlinson had the pleasure of finding four circles in a field opposite his house in the Cotswolds. His barograph displayed significant changes at the presumed time of formation in the early daylight hours. Other barographs in the locality confirmed this, so it seems that the circles may have been created in conjunction with a minor frontal passage. Fronts were detected in connection with circle appearances at various sites on other days too. On one occasion a retrograding sea-breeze front was certainly involved. In all cases the air was nearly still before the arrival of the frontal boundary.

A week-long circles watch was undertaken at a site in Wiltshire at the start of July (Operation Green Hill). On most nights manning was continuous, but regrettably no observers were present when circles appeared in full view of the main watchpoint between midnight and 10 a.m. on 4th July. Voluntary observers would again be welcome this summer, especially those who can bring along or attend to scientific and photographic apparatus.

A circle at Mansfield in Nottinghamshire, surveyed by Jenny Randles, was potentially important for an unusual reason. This 5½-m circle in a field of oats was reportedly centred exactly where drilling equipment had operated three years earlier. This implies that in its final stage of descent the vortex homed in on buried metal, which suggests that the electrified vortex was directed to it by local changes in electric and magnetic fields (much as a stroke of lightning in the final stage of its downward passage can be redirected towards a lightning conductor).

Also theoretically important is that ten, at least, of this year's circles had stalks at their centres structured into prominent pyramids. This is plain proof of a *ring* vortex striking the crop, which signifies the development of a breakdown state of a primary vortex condition such as a hill-sourced trailing vortex. In this connection Prof. John Snow (U.S.A.) drew attention to a relevant paper by N. Tamai, T. Asaeda and N. Tanaka (Japan) published in *Boundary Layer Meteorology* in 1987 (vol. 39, 301-314). These researchers performed fluid-flow experiments involving laminar motion over a hemispherical hill, and showed how stable, arched vortex tubes develop in the downstream turbulence. Flowing water coloured with dye was used, but a similar result would be expected for laminar airflow across a real hill. Another paper pertinent to atmospheric vortex stability appeared in *Nature* in April 1989: 'Tripolar vortices in a rotating fluid'. The authors, G. H. F. Van Heijst and R. C. Kloosterziel, demonstrated by means of laboratory experiments how a monopolar vortex in the sheared environment of a rapidly-rotating fluid reforms into a previously-unknown stable, tri-polar state. This effect may be related to the in-line triple vortices that we have noted in the circles effect (cf figures on pp. 10 and 41).

While in Tokyo in September 1989 to give a keynote lecture at a symposium of the 'Union Radio-Scientifique Internationale' [Discovery of a new electromagnetic phenomenon in the atmosphere: the plasma vortex and its physical properties as revealed by patterned ground traces and radio-frequency, electromagnetic, acoustic and luminous effects. Proc. URSI Conference (to be published)], the present author met physicists working in the areas of space and environmental electromagnetics and plasma physics who were attracted by the circles problem. These included atmospheric-ionization expert Professor Hiroshi Kikuchi and ball-lightning expert Professor Y. H. Ohtsuki who agreed about meteorologically-formed plasma vortices as being at the origin of the circles effect and its related ball-of-light phenomena. Another meteorologist who is studying this topic is Dr Tokio Kikuchi, a specialist in the origin of wind-flow traces seen on snow surfaces in the Antarctic. Some of these scientists, and others, will assist at the World's First Circles Effect Conference in Oxford on 23 June 1990 (of which the proceedings will be published by Artetech the same month under the title *Circles Research 1*), and some will attend the Second International Ball Lightning Conference in Budapest the following week.

This summary has necessarily been much abbreviated. Further details are given in papers in *J. Meteorology*, especially in issues dated August, October, November and December 1989, and January 1990 et seq.

January 1990   G. TERENCE MEADEN

INDEX

Multi-layering, 14, 17, 70.
Multi-set circle systems, 63-66.
Multi-set formation, time sequence 65-66.

Newbottle tornado ball of light, 49.
Nitrogen emission spectrum, 60.
Nocturnal vortices, 4-41, 53, 54, 66, 69, 74-78, 79-80, 93-98.

Oadby, Leicester, tri-symmetric quadruplet, 19, 63, Figure 31.
Optical effects, 33-35, 51-56.
Orientation test, 89-90.
Outbreaks of like circles, 97.

Paranormal, 88-89.
Patterns, circular, 9-14 and passim.
Perimeters, 70-72, 84.
Physiological effects, 29, 51, 83-84.
Piezoelectricity, 88,
Plasma, 48, 57-59, 92-97, 104.
Plasma vortex or plasmoid, 48, 49, 60, 74-75, 80, 85, 93-97, 104.
Positively-charged plasmoids, 94.
Prester tornado, 48-49.
Property damage, 29-31.
Pulse-generator, tornado, 50; the 'plasmoid vortex', 54.
Pulsed ball of light, (USA), 98.
Punchbowl or concave hill-slopes, 40-41.

Quadri-symmetric circle sets, see quintuplets.
Quadruplet, as incomplete quintuplet, Figure 3.
Quadruplets, (tri-symmetric at Oadby) 63, Figure 3 and 31.
Quintuplets, 63-66, 90-92, 95.

Radar angels, 99.
Radial symmetry (starburst effect), 18-20, 50, 94.
Radio-communication interference, 50-51, 77-78, 95, 96.
Rainwater, 41-42, 97.
Ringed circles, 16 (A.D. 1678), 20-23, 60-63, 96.
Rings, sharpness, 84-85, 96.
Rings without circles, 67-69.

S-shaped beds, 14, 71, 94.
Safety of aircraft, 99.
Saint Souplet circle and light, 52.
Scorching effects, 35, 51 (tornadoes), 54 (Sharnbrook).
Sea-breeze fronts, 108.
Sferics, 50-51.
Sharnbrook blast, 54, 106.
Silbury circles, 55-56.
Silbury pipe or tube, 55-56.
Spikes, 71.
Spinning top, 43.
Spirals, 13-14, 16-18, 26-27, 91-92, 98.
Spirals, non-centred, 16.
Spurs, 23-24, 42, 72-73.